Ruizhong Hu
Jianming Liu
Mingguo Zhai

Mineral Resources Science in China: A Roadmap to 2050

Chinese Academy of Sciences

Ruizhong Hu
Jianming Liu
Mingguo Zhai
Editors

Mineral Resources Science in China: A Roadmap to 2050

With 19 figures

Science Press
Beijing

Springer

Editors

Ruizhong Hu
Institute of Geochemistry, CAS
550002, Guiyang, China
E-mail: huruizhong@vip.gyig.ac.cn

Jianming Liu
Institute of Geology and Geophysics, CAS
100029, Beijing, China
E-mail: jmliu@mail.igcas.ac.cn

Mingguo Zhai
Institute of Geology and Geophysics, CAS
100029, Beijing, China
E-mail: mgzhai@mail.igcas.ac.cn

ISBN 978-7-03-026409-1
Science Press Beijing

ISBN 978-3-642-05343-6 e-ISBN 978-3-642-05344-3
Springer Heidelberg Dordrecht London New York

Library of Congress Control Number: 2009937448

Cover design: Frido Steinen-Broo, EStudio Calamar, Spain

Printed on acid-free paper

Springer is a part of Springer Science+Business Media (www.springer.com)

Members of the Editorial Committee and the Editorial Office

Editor-in-Chief

Editorial Committee

Research Group on Mineral Resources of the Chinese Academy of Sciences

Head: Ruizhong Hu

Deputy head: Jianming Liu

Members: (In the alphabetical order of Chinese surname)

Xianwu Bi	Institute of Geochemistry, the Chinese Academy of Sciences
Xinbin Feng	Institute of Geochemistry, the Chinese Academy of Sciences
Ruizhong Hu	Institute of Geochemistry, the Chinese Academy of Sciences
Peng Huang	Institute of Oceanology, the Chinese Academy of Sciences
Chunlai Li	National Astronomical Observatories, the Chinese Academy of Sciences
Haoran Li	Institute of Process Engineering, the Chinese Academy of Sciences
Jianming Liu	Institute of Geology and Geophysics, the Chinese Academy of Sciences
Shen Liu	Institute of Geochemistry, the Chinese Academy of Sciences
Fengshan Ma	Institute of Geology and Geophysics, the Chinese Academy of Sciences
Xieyan Song	Institute of Geochemistry, the Chinese Academy of Sciences
Weidong Sun	Guangzhou Institute of Geochemistry, the Chinese Academy of Sciences
Yan Tao	Institute of Geochemistry, the Chinese Academy of Sciences
Yonglan Xiong	National Science Library, the Chinese Academy of Sciences
Mingguo Zhai	Institute of Geology and Geophysics, the Chinese Academy of Sciences
Qian Zhang	Institute of Geochemistry, the Chinese Academy of Sciences
Xingchun Zhang	Institute of Geochemistry, the Chinese Academy of Sciences
Shaoping Zhou	Bureau of Science and Technology for Resources and Environment, the Chinese Academy of Sciences

Foreword to the Roadmaps 2050*

China's modernization is viewed as a transformative revolution in the human history of modernization. As such, the Chinese Academy of Sciences (CAS) decided to give higher priority to the research on the science and technology (S&T) roadmap for priority areas in China's modernization process. What is the purpose? And why is it? Is it a must? I think those are substantial and significant questions to start things forward.

Significance of the Research on China's S&T Roadmap to 2050

We are aware that the National Mid- and Long-term S&T Plan to 2020 has already been formed after two years' hard work by a panel of over 2000 experts and scholars brought together from all over China, chaired by Premier Wen Jiabao. This clearly shows that China has already had its S&T blueprint to 2020. Then, why did CAS conduct this research on China's S&T roadmap to 2050?

In the summer of 2007 when CAS was working out its future strategic priorities for S&T development, it realized that some issues, such as energy, must be addressed with a long-term view. As a matter of fact, some strategic researches have been conducted, over the last 15 years, on energy, but mainly on how to best use of coal, how to best exploit both domestic and international oil and gas resources, and how to develop nuclear energy in a discreet way. Renewable energy was, of course, included but only as a supplementary energy. It was not yet thought as a supporting leg for future energy development. However, greenhouse gas emissions are becoming a major world concern over

---

* It is adapted from a speech by President Yongxiang Lu at the first High-level Workshop on China's S&T Roadmap for Priority Areas to 2050, organized by the Chinese Academy of Sciences, in October, 2007.

the years, and how to address the global climate change has been on the agenda. In fact, what is really behind is the concern for energy structure, which makes us realize that fossil energy must be used cleanly and efficiently in order to reduce its impact on the environment. However, fossil energy is, pessimistically speaking, expected to be used up within about 100 years, or optimistically speaking, within about 200 years. Oil and gas resources may be among the first to be exhausted, and then coal resources follow. When this happens, human beings will have to refer to renewable energy as its major energy, while nuclear energy as a supplementary one. Under this situation, governments of the world are taking preparatory efforts in this regard, with Europe taking the lead and the USA shifting to take a more positive attitude, as evidenced in that: while fossil energy has been taken the best use of, renewable energy has been greatly developed, and the R&D of advanced nuclear energy has been reinforced with the objective of being eventually transformed into renewable energy. The process may last 50 to 100 years or so. Hence, many S&T problems may come around. In the field of basic research, for example, research will be conducted by physicists, chemists and biologists on the new generation of photovoltaic cell, dye-sensitized solar cells (DSC), high-efficient photochemical catalysis and storage, and efficient photosynthetic species, or high-efficient photosynthetic species produced by gene engineering which are free from land and water demands compared with food and oil crops, and can be grown on hillside, saline lands and semi-arid places, producing the energy that fits humanity. In the meantime, although the existing energy system is comparatively stable, future energy structure is likely to change into an unstable system. Presumably, dispersive energy system as well as higher-efficient direct current transmission and storage technology will be developed, so will be the safe and reliable control of network, and the capture, storage, transfer and use of CO_2, all of which involve S&T problems in almost all scientific disciplines. Therefore, it is natural that energy problems may bring out both basic and applied research, and may eventually lead to comprehensive structural changes. And this may last for 50 to 100 years or so. Taking the nuclear energy as an example, it usually takes about 20 years or more from its initial plan to key technology breakthroughs, so does the subsequent massive application and commercialization. If we lose the opportunity to make foresighted arrangements, we will be lagging far behind in the future. France has already worked out the roadmap to 2040 and 2050 respectively for the development of the 3rd and 4th generation of nuclear fission reactors, while China has not yet taken any serious actions. Under this circumstance, it is now time for CAS to take the issue seriously, for the sake of national interests, and to start conducting a foresighted research in this regard.

This strategic research covers over some dozens of areas with a long-term view. Taking agriculture as an example, our concern used to be limited only to the increased production of high-quality food grains and agricultural by-products. However, in the future, the main concern will definitely be given to the water-saving and ecological agriculture. As China is vast in territory, diversified technologies in this regard are the appropriate solutions. Animal husbandry has been used by developed countries, such as Japan and Denmark, to make bioreactor and pesticide as well. Plants have been used by Japan to make bioreactors which are safer and cost-effective than that made from animals. Potato, strawberry, tomato and the like have been bred in germ-free greenhouses, and value-added products have been made through gene transplantation technology. Agriculture in China must not only address the food demands from its one billions-plus population, but also take into consideration of the value-added agriculture by-products and the high-tech development of agriculture as well. Agriculture in the future is expected to bring out some energies and fuels needed by both industry and man's livelihood as well. Some developed countries have taken an earlier start to conduct foresighted research in this regard, while we have not yet taken sufficient consideration.

Population is another problem. It will be most likely that China's population will not drop to about 1 billion until the end of this century, given that the past mistakes of China's population policy be rectified. But the subsequent problem of ageing could only be sorted out until the next century. The current population and health policies face many challenges, such as, how to ensure that the 1.3 to 1.5 billion people enjoy fair and basic public healthcare; the necessity to develop advanced and public healthcare and treatment technologies; and the change of research priority to chronic diseases from infectious diseases, as developed countries have already started research in this regard under the increasing social and environmental change. There are many such research problems yet to be sorted out by starting from the basic research, and subsequent policies within the next 50 years are in need to be worked out.

Space and oceans provide humanity with important resources for future development. In terms of space research, the well-known Manned Spacecraft Program and China's Lunar Exploration Program will last for 20 or 25 years. But what will be the whole plan for China's space technology? What is the objective? Will it just follow the suit of developed countries? It is worth doing serious study in this regard. The present spacecraft is mainly sent into space with chemical fuel propellant rocket. Will this traditional propellant still be used in future deep space exploration? Or other new technologies such as electrical propellant, nuclear energy propellant, and solar sail technologies be developed? We haven't yet done any strategic research over these issues, not even worked out any plans. The ocean is abundant in mineral resources, oil and gas, natural gas hydrate, biological resources, energy and photo-free biological evolution, which may arise our scientific interests. At present, many countries have worked out new strategic marine plans. Russia, Canada, the USA, Sweden and Norway have centered their contention upon the North Pole, an area of strategic significance. For this, however, we have only limited plans.

The national and public security develops with time, and covers both conventional and non-conventional security. Conventional security threats only refer to foreign invasion and warfare, while, the present security threat may come out from any of the natural, man-made, external, interior, ecological, environmental, and the emerging networking (including both real and virtual) factors. The conflicts out of these must be analyzed from the perspective of human civilization, and be sorted out in a scientific manner. Efforts must be made to root out the cause of the threats, while human life must be treasured at any time.

In general, it is necessary to conduct this strategic research in view of the future development of China and mankind as well. The past 250 years' industrialization has resulted in the modernization and better-off life of less than 1 billion people, predominantly in Europe, North America, Japan and Singapore. The next 50 years' modernization drive will definitely lead to a better-off life for 2–3 billion people, including over 1 billion Chinese, doubling or tripling the economic increase over that of the past 250 years, which will, on the one hand, bring vigor and vitality to the world, and, on the other hand, inevitably challenge the limited resources and eco-environment on the earth. New development mode must be shaped so that everyone on the earth will be able to enjoy fairly the achievements of modern civilization. Achieving this requires us, in the process of China's modernization, to have a foresighted overview on the future development of world science and human civilization, and on how science and technology could serve the modernization drive. S&T roadmap for priority areas to 2050 must be worked out, and solutions to core science problems and key technology problems must be straightened out, which will eventually provide consultations for the nation's S&T decision-making.

Possibility of Working out China's S&T Roadmap to 2050

Some people held the view that science is hard to be predicted as it happens unexpectedly and mainly comes out of scientists' innovative thinking, while, technology might be predicted but at the maximum of 15 years. In my view, however, S&T foresight in some areas seems feasible. For instance, with the exhaustion of fossil energy, some smart people may think of transforming solar energy into energy-intensive biomass through improved high-efficient solar thin-film materials and devices, or even developing new substitute. As is driven by huge demands, many investments will go to this emerging area. It is, therefore, able to predict that, in the next 50 years, some breakthroughs will undoubtedly be made in the areas of renewable energy and nuclear energy as well. In terms of solar energy, for example, the improvement of photoelectric conversion efficiency and photothermal conversion efficiency will be the focus. Of course, the concrete technological solutions may be varied, for example, by changing the morphology of the surface of solar cells and through the reflection, the entire spectrum can be absorbed more efficiently; by developing multi-layer functional thin-films for transmission and absorption; or by introducing of nanotechnology and quantum control technology, etc. Quantum control research used to limit mainly to the solution to information functional materials. This is surely too narrow. In the future, this research is expected to be extended to the energy issue or energy-based basic research in cutting-edge areas.

In terms of computing science, we must be confident to forecast its future development instead of simply following suit as we used to. This is a possibility rather than wild fancies. Information scientists, physicists and biologists could be engaged in the forward-looking research. In 2007, the Nobel Physics Prize was awarded to the discovery of colossal magneto-resistance, which was, however, made some 20 years ago. Today, this technology has already been applied to hard disk store. Our conclusion made, at this stage, is that: it is possible to make long-term and unconventional S&T predictions, and so is it to work out China's S&T roadmap in view of long-term strategies, for example, by 2020 as the first step, by 2030 or 2035 as the second step, and by 2050 as the maximum.

This possibility may also apply to other areas of research. The point is to emancipate the mind and respect objective laws rather than indulging in wild fancies. We attribute our success today to the guidelines of emancipating the mind and seeking the truth from the facts set by the Third Plenary Session of the 11th Central Committee of the Communist Party of China in 1979. We must break the conventional barriers and find a way of development fitting into China's reality. The history of science tells us that discoveries and breakthroughs could only be made when you open up your mind, break the conventional barriers, and make foresighted plans. Top-down guidance on research with increased financial support and involvement of a wider range of talented scientists is not in conflict with demand-driven research and free discovery of science as well.

Necessity of CAS Research on China's S&T Roadmap to 2050

Why does CAS launch this research? As is known, CAS is the nation's highest academic institution in natural sciences. It targets at making basic, forward-looking and strategic research and playing a leading role in China's science. As such, how can it achieve this if without a foresighted view on science and technology? From the perspective of CAS, it is obligatory to think, with a global view, about what to do after the 3rd Phase of the Knowledge Innovation Program (KIP). Shall we follow the way as it used to? Or shall we, with a view of national interests, present our in-depth insights into different research disciplines, and make efforts to reform the organizational structure and system, so that the innovation capability of CAS and the nation's science and technology mission will be raised to a new height? Clearly, the latter is more positive. World science and technology develops at a lightening speed. As global economy grows, we are aware that we will be lagging far behind if without making progress, and will lose the opportunity if without making foresighted plans. S&T innovation requires us to make joint efforts, break the conventional barriers and emancipate the mind. This is also what we need for further development.

The roadmap must be targeted at the national level so that the strategic research reports will form an important part of the national long-term program. CAS may not be able to fulfill all the objectives in the reports. However, it can select what is able to do and make foresighted plans, which will eventually help shape the post-2010 research priorities of CAS and the guidelines for its future reform.

Once the long-term roadmap and its objectives are identified, system mechanism, human resources, funding and allocation should be ensured for full implementation. We will make further studies to figure out: What will happen to world innovation system within the next 30 to 50 years? Will universities, research institutions and enterprises still be included in the system? Will research institutes become grid structure? When the cutting-edge research combines basic science and high-tech and the transformative research integrates the cutting-edge research with industrialization, will that be the research trend in some disciplines? What will be the changes for personnel structure, motivation mechanism and upgrading mechanism within the innovation system? Will there be any changes for the input and structure of innovation resources? If we could have a clear mind of all the questions, make foresighted plans and then dare to try out in relevant CAS institutes, we will be able to pave a way for a more competitive and smooth development.

Social changes are without limit, so are the development of science and technology, and innovation system and management as well. CAS must keep moving ahead to make foresighted plans not only for science and technology, but also for its organizational structure, human resources, management modes, and resource structures. By doing so, CAS will keep standing at the forefront of science and playing a leading role in the national innovation system, and even, frankly speaking, taking the lead in some research disciplines in the world. This is, in fact, our purpose of conducting the strategic research on China's S&T roadmap.

Prof. Dr.-Ing. Yongxiang Lu

President of the Chinese Academy of Sciences

Preface to the Roadmaps 2050

CAS is the nation's think tank for science. Its major responsibility is to provide S&T consultations for the nation's decision-makings and to take the lead in the nation's S&T development.

In July, 2007, President Yongxiang Lu made the following remarks: "In order to carry out the Scientific Outlook of Development through innovation, further strategic research should be done to lay out a S&T roadmap for the next 20–30 years and key S&T innovation disciplines. And relevant workshops should be organized with the participation of scientists both within CAS and outside to further discuss the research priorities and objectives. We should no longer confine ourselves to the free discovery of science, the quantity and quality of scientific papers, nor should we satisfy ourselves simply with the Principal Investigators system of research. Research should be conducted to address the needs of both the nation and society, in particular, the continued growth of economy and national competitiveness, the development of social harmony, and the sustainability between man and nature. "

According to the Executive Management Committee of CAS in July, 2007, CAS strategic research on S&T roadmap for future development should be conducted to orchestrate the needs of both the nation and society, and target at the three objectives: the growth of economy and national competitiveness, the development of social harmony, and the sustainability between man and nature.

In August, 2007, President Yongxiang Lu further put it: "Strategic research requires a forward-looking view over the world, China, and science & technology in 2050. Firstly, in terms of the world in 2050, we should be able to study the perspectives of economy, society, national security, eco-environment, and science & technology, specifically in such scientific disciplines as energy, resources, population, health, information, security, eco-environment, space and oceans. And we should be aware of where the opportunities and challenges lie. Secondly, in terms of China's economy and society in 2050, we should take into consideration of factors like: objectives, methods, and scientific supports needed for economic structure, social development, energy structure, population and health, eco-environment, national security and innovation capability. Thirdly, in terms of the guidance of Scientific Outlook of Development on science and technology, it emphasizes the people's interests and development, science and technology, science and economy, science and society, science and eco-environment, science and culture, innovation and collaborative development. Fourthly, in terms of the supporting role of research in scientific development, this includes how to optimize the economic structure and boost economy, agricultural development, energy structure, resource conservation, recycling economy, knowledge-based society, harmonious coexistence between man and nature, balance of regional development, social harmony, national security, and international cooperation. Based on these, the role of CAS will be further identified."

Subsequently, CAS launched its strategic research on the roadmap for priority areas to 2050, which comes into eighteen categories including: energy, water resources, mineral resources, marine resources, oil and gas, population and health, agriculture, eco-environment, biomass resources, regional development, space, information, advanced manufacturing, advanced materials, nano-science, big science facilities, cross-disciplinary and frontier research, and national and public security. Over 300 CAS experts in science, technology, management and documentation & information, including about 60 CAS members, from over 80 CAS institutes joined this research.

Over one year's hard work, substantial progress has been made in each research group of the scientific disciplines. The strategic demands on priority areas in China's modernization drive to 2050 have been strengthened out; some core science problems and key technology problems been set forth; a relevant S&T roadmap been worked out based on China's reality; and eventually the strategic reports on China's S&T roadmap for eighteen priority areas to 2050 been formed. Under the circumstance, both the Editorial Committee and Writing Group, chaired by President Yongxiang Lu, have finalized the general report. The research reports are to be published in the form of CAS strategic research serial reports, entitled *Science and Technology Roadmap to China 2050: Strategic Reports of the Chinese Academy of Sciences.*

The unique feature of this strategic research is its use of S&T roadmap approach. S&T roadmap differs from the commonly used planning and technology foresight in that it includes science and technology needed for the future, the roadmap to reach the objectives, description of environmental changes, research needs, technology trends, and innovation and technology development. Scientific planning in the form of roadmap will have a clearer scientific objective, form closer links with the market, projects selected be more interactive and systematic, the solutions to the objective be defined, and the plan be more feasible. In addition, by drawing from both the foreign experience on roadmap research and domestic experience on strategic planning, we have formed our own ways of making S&T roadmap in priority areas as follows:

(1) Establishment of organization mechanism for strategic research on S&T roadmap for priority areas

The Editorial Committee is set up with the head of President Yongxiang Lu and the involvement of Chunli Bai, Erwei Shi, Xin Fang, Zhigang Li, Xiaoye Cao and Jiaofeng Pan. And the Writing Group was organized to take responsibility of the research and writing of the general report. CAS Bureau of Planning and Strategy, as the executive unit, coordinates the research, selects the scholars, identifies concrete steps and task requirements, sets forth research approaches, and organizes workshops and independent peer reviews of the research, in order to ensure the smooth progress of the strategic research on the S&T roadmap for priority areas.

(2) Setting up principles for the S&T roadmap for priority areas

The framework of roadmap research should be targeted at the national level, and divided into three steps as immediate-term (by 2020), mid-term (by 2030) and long-term (by 2050). It should cover the description of job requirements, objectives, specific tasks, research approaches, and highlight core science problems and key technology problems, which must be, in general, directional, strategic and feasible.

(3) Selection of expertise for strategic research on the S&T roadmap

Scholars in science policy, management, information and documentation, and chief scientists of the middle-aged and the young should be selected to form a special research group. The head of the group should be an outstanding scientist with a strategic vision, strong sense of responsibility and coordinative capability. In order to steer the research direction, chief scientists should be selected as the core members of the group to ensure that the strategic research in priority areas be based on the cutting-edge and frontier research. Information and documentation scholars should be engaged in each research group to guarantee the efficiency and systematization of the research through data collection and analysis. Science policy scholars should focus on the strategic demands and their feasibility.

(4) Organization of regular workshops at different levels

Workshops should be held as a leverage to identify concrete research steps and ensure its smooth progress. Five workshops have been organized consecutively in the following forms:

High-level Workshop on S&T Strategies. Three workshops on S&T strategies have been organized in October, 2007, December, 2007, and June, 2008, respectively, with the participation of research group heads in eighteen priority areas, chief scholars, and relevant top CAS management members. Information has been exchanged, and consensus been reached to ensure research directions. During the workshops, President Yongxiang Lu pinpointed the significance, necessity and possibility of the roadmap research, and commented on the work of each research groups, thus pushing the research forward.

Special workshops. The Editorial Committee invited science policy scholars to the special workshops to discuss the eight basic and strategic systems for China's socio-economic development. Perspectives on China's science-driven modernization to 2050 and characteristics and objectives of the eight systems have been outlined, and twenty-two strategic S&T problems affecting the modernization have been figured out.

Research group workshops. Each research group was further divided into different research teams based on different disciplines. Group discussions, team discussions and cross-team discussions were organized for further research, occasionally with the involvement of related scholars in special topic discussions. Research group workshops have been held some 70 times.

Cross-group workshops. Cross-group and cross-disciplinary workshops were organized, with the initiation by relative research groups and coordination by Bureau of Planning and Strategies, to coordinate the research in relative disciplines.

Professional workshops. These workshops were held to have the suggestions and advices of both domestic and international professionals over the development and strategies in related disciplines.

(5) Establishment of a peer review mechanism for the roadmap research

To ensure the quality of research reports and enhance coordination among different disciplines, a workshop on the peer review of strategic research on the S&T roadmap was organized by CAS Bureau of Planning and Strategy, in November, 2008, bringing together of about 30 peer review experts and 50 research group scholars. The review was made in four different categories, namely, resources and environment, strategic high-technology, bio-science & technology, and basic research. Experts listened to the reports of different research groups, commented on the general structure, what's new and existing problems, and presented their suggestions and advices. The outcomes were put in the written forms and returned to the research groups for further revisions.

(6) Establishment of a sustained mechanism for the roadmap research

To cope with the rapid change of world science and technology and national demands, a roadmap is, by nature, in need of sustained study, and should be revised once in every 3–5 years. Therefore, a panel of science policy scholars should be formed to keep a constant watch on the priority areas and key S&T problems for the nation's long-term benefits and make further study in this regard. And hopefully, more science policy scholars will be trained out of the research process.

The serial reports by CAS have their contents firmly based on China's reality while keeping the future in view. The work is a crystallization of the scholars' wisdom, written in a careful and scrupulous manner. Herewith, our sincere gratitude goes to all the scholars engaged in the research, consultation and review. It is their joint efforts and hard work that help to enable the serial reports to be published for the public within only one year.

To precisely predict the future is extremely challenging. This strategic research covered a wide range of areas and time, and adopted new research approaches. As such, the serial reports may have its deficiency due to the limit in knowledge and assessment. We, therefore, welcome timely advice and enlightening remarks from a much wider circle of scholars around the world.

The publication of the serial reports is a new start instead of the end of the strategic research. With this, we will further our research in this regard, duly release the research results, and have the roadmap revised every five years, in an effort to provide consultations to the state decision-makers in science, and give suggestions to science policy departments, research institutions, enterprises, and universities for their S&T policy-making. Raising the public awareness of science and technology is of great significance for China's modernization.

Writing Group of the General Report

February, 2009

Preface

In 2007, Chinese Academy of Sciences (CAS) launched researches on roadmaps for scientific and technological development in 18 major areas from present to 2050. A project team for mineral resources has carried out, in accordance with the requirements that "the report on strategic roadmap researches should reflect the strategy, orientation and operability" proposed by President Lu and Bureau of Planning & Strategy of the CAS, researches on "a roadmap for scientific and technological development of solid mineral resources in China from present to 2050". The work is mainly listed below.

1) Various research data and reports related to the project have been searched and collected to provide basic information for drawing a roadmap for scientific and technological development of mineral resources.

2) The future China's demands on mineral resources have been predicted through the information research and relevant analysis based on the characteristics of socioeconomic development and the depletion speed of mineral resources in China.

3) The potential of mineral resources in China has been evaluated based on geological characteristics of China.

4) The Project Team has held five meetings of team members and two workshops of the team members and other senior specialists. In addition, the team members have attended two workshops organized by the CAS. The team members have adsorbed relevant research achievements and reached their common understandings through these academic activities, therefore, the research of the project has been promoted.

5) According to consumption demands of mineral resources in future China, the potential of mineral resources in China, and the development trend of science and technology, the overall objectives and the objectives in various stages in mineral resources field from present to 2050 have been set up. The major development orientation of science and technology coordinated with the development objectives of mineral resources, the major scientific and technological issues, which should be or must be resolved, and their corresponding policies and measures have been proposed and pointed.

The research field of this report is only limited to solid mineral resources.

It is well known that there are numerous kinds of solid mineral resources in China. For example, about 170 kinds of solid mineral resources have been discovered, and about 160 kinds of mineral resources have figures of proved reserves at present. Therefore, only a few kinds of mineral resources (e.g., iron, copper, aluminum, etc), were specifically concerned. Other kinds of solid mineral resources were treated as one object to have been described in this report.

Prof. Ruizhong Hu (Institute of Geochemistry, the Chinese Academy of Sciences) has been appointed as the head of this project team, and Prof. Jianming Liu (Institute of Geology and Geophysics, the Chinese Academy of Sciences) has been appointed as deputy head. Other members of the team include Prof. Xianwu Bi, Qian Zhang, Xinbin Feng, Xieyan Song, Yan Tao, Shen Liu, Xingchun Zhang (Institute of Geochemistry, the Chinese Academy of Sciences), Mingguo Zhai, Fengshan Ma (Institute of Geology and Geophysics, the Chinese Academy of Sciences), Shaoping Zhou (Bureau of Science and Technology for Resources and Environment, the Chinese Academy of Sciences), Haoran Li (Institute of Process Engineering, the Chinese Academy of Sciences), Chunlai Li (National Astronomical Observatories, the Chinese Academy of Sciences), Weidong Sun (Guangzhou Institute of Geochemistry, the Chinese Academy of Sciences), Yonglan Xiong (National Science Library, the Chinese Academy of Sciences) and Peng Huang (Institute of Oceanology, the Chinese Academy of Sciences). The preface, abstract, conclusion, postscript, situation of mineral resources in China, and the overview of a roadmap for scientific and technological development of solid mineral resources in China from present to 2050 were written by Ruizhong Hu. The part of report on metallogenic theories and regularities was written by Ruizhong Hu and Xianwu Bi. The part on prospecting, forecast and exploration of mineral resources was written by Jianming Liu and Ruizhong Hu. The part on clean and efficient utilization of mineral resources was written by Haoran Li and Xinbin Feng. The part on substitute of mineral resources and cyclic utilization of used mineral resources was written by Jianming Liu. The part on global allocation of mineral resources was written by Jianming Liu, Mingguo Zhai and Qian Zhang. The part on policies required to attain objectives was written by Ruizhong Hu, Shaoping Zhou and Xinbin Feng. This report was finalized by Ruizhong Hu and Jianming Liu.

We are very grateful to the following academicians and professors. including Ziyuan Ouyang, Yunshan Qin, Danian Ye, Yusheng Zhai, Jiwen Teng, Congbin Fu, Wenhua Li and Zhongli Ding; Profs. Bojie Fu, Weiming Fan, Xu Chang, Jingbin Wang, Yuansheng Li, Jinyi Guo, Yanjing Chen, Qian Gao, Weixuan Fang, Yongsheng Song and Zhigang Zeng; Xiaoye Cao, vice secretary-general of the CAS, Jiaofeng Pan, director of the Bureau of Planning & Strategy of the CAS, Feng Zheng and Wenyuan Wang, section chiefs of the Bureau of Planning & Strategy of the CAS, for their valuable suggestions and advises.

Contents

Abstract

Mineral resources represent the key material basis for the socio-economic development. Exploitation and utilization of mineral resources are the essential requirement for modernization. There are two basic and real contradictions in the field of mineral resources in China. One contradiction is between the great demand for mineral resources and the shortage of the proved reserves of major minerals. The other is among the huge potential of mineral prospecting, insufficient utilization of mineral resources, the prominent environmental challenges by mineral exploitation, and the relative low level of research, exploration and exploitation on deposits. At present, the key issue is how to tap the huge potential of mineral resources, and to improve their utilization efficiency, consequently, to relieve the situation of severe shortage of proved reserves of major mineral resources in China, furthermore, to secure the coordinated development between exploitation and utilization of mineral resources and the construction of ecological environment. In our view, in order to resolve the above problems, many corresponding measures, such as, the rational utilization of international resources, reduction of minerals consumption for unit output and improvement of mining management should be regarded. In addition, on the basis of the systematic cognition on the unique evolution history of the lithosphere beneath China, we should focus on three scientific questions related to the research on metallogenic theories and rules, i.e., the accumulation process of huge volumes of ore-forming materials, the spatial and temporal distribution regularities of deposits and the relationship between metallogenic model and prospecting model. Moreover, we should make breakthroughs in three important technical directions including the prospecting of concealed mineral resources in covered areas and in depth, the clean and efficient utilization of mineral resources, the substitute and recycling utilization of mineral resources. In addition, the integration, test, demonstration and application of relevant technologies should be improved.

The short, middle and long terms strategic blueprints are given below. From present to 2020, our objective is firstly to determine the metallogenic rules and prospecting prospects in major metallogenic regions and belts, to make breakthroughs in accurate element determination technology on site, aerogeophysical technology, high-precision technology for extracting metallogenic information, and the high-resolution geophysical technology prospecting mineral resources in depth (up to 2,000m in depth) in eastern China. Secondly, our objective is to improve the recovery rates of mineral resources in processes of mining, processing and smelting in major mines, as well as the rates of comprehensive utilization of the symbiotic and associated deposits. Thirdly, our objective is to undertake the pilot research and development on the technology for substituting some kinds of mineral resources with shortage reserves. Fourthly, our objective is to make breakthroughs in technology for efficient recycling of used metals. Fifthly, it is to improve the ecological environments of mines in China. From 2020 to 2030, we should be able to establish the continental metallogenic theoretical system of China; to make breakthroughs in technologies for efficient and high-precision exploring mineral resources within 2,000m in depth in western China, for clean and efficient utilizing low-grade ores and tailings, and for making fertilizer with non-water-soluble potassium resources, to basically restore the ecological environment of historical abandoned mines, and eventually to control the environmental pollutions. From 2030 to 2050, we should be able to unravel the relationship between the Earth system and metallogenic system, to make breakthroughs on the technology for exploring mineral resources within 3,000–4,000m in depth, to develop a series of core technologies for clean and efficient utilization of mineral resources, to make breakthroughs in technology for substituting common metal materials by silicate fiber, and finally, to build a system for the sustainable supply and utilization of mineral resource in China, and to secure the coordinated development between the exploitation and utilization of mineral resources and construction of ecological environment.

The main indexes set for various periods are given below. Until 2020, the rate of proved reserves of major mineral resources in deep earth (up to 2,000m in depth) in eastern and central China should reach 50%. The total recovery of mineral resources should reach 50%. The rate of comprehensive utilization rate of mineral resources should be 45%. The energy consumption should be reduced by 20%. The discharges of waste gas, waste water and industrial residue ("three wastes") should drop down by 30%. The ecological environment of 45% historical abandoned mines in China should be rehabilitated, and the environment of 30% polluted mining area should be restored. Land reclamation rate in new mines should reach 100%. The rate of alternative and cyclic utilization of the crucial mineral resources should reach 20–40%. From 2020 to 2030, the rate of proved reserves of mineral resources within 2,000m in depth in western China should meet 50%. The total recovery of mineral resources should attain 70%. The rate of comprehensive utilization of mineral resources should reach 60%. The energy consumption should be reduced by 30%. The discharges of "three wastes" should drop down by 50%. The ecological environment of 65% historical abandoned mines should be rehabilitated, and the environment of 50% polluted mining areas should be restored. The rate of alternative and recycling of the crucial mineral resources should achieve 30–50%. From 2030 to 2050, the rate of proved reserves of mineral resources in depth between 3,000m and 4,000m in China should meet 70%. The total recovery of mineral resources should reach 80%. The rate of comprehensive utilization of mineral resources should be 80%. The rate of energy consumption per unit should be reduced by 50%. The rate of discharges of "three wastes" should drop down by 80%. The ecological environmental damage and pollutions caused by mining, processing, smelting and other processes mining industry should be properly controlled. The rate of alternative and cyclic utilization of the crucial mineral resources should achieve to 40–60%.

1 Situation of Mineral Resources in China

Mineral resources are the key material basis for the socio-economic development. Statistical results show that more than 95% of energy used by mankind, 80% industrial raw materials and 70% raw materials for agricultural production are from mineral resources. Due to the advancement of world industrialization, it is predicted that global demands on mineral resources will be increased continuously in the next decades. Therefore, how to meet the demands on mineral resources for sustainable development has become one of key issues in the world.

China holds diversified and large-scale mineral resources. There are 171 kinds of mineral resources in China, with proved reserves for 159 kinds of mineral resources. The proved reserves of mineral resources occupy 12% of the total mineral resources in the world, ranking in third position below USA and Russia. More than 20 kinds of mineral resources in China are ranked in the forefront of the world. For example, the proved reserves of twelve minerals (tungsten, tin, antimony, rare earths, titanium, magnesium, etc.) are ranked in first position among countries of the world for respective kinds of minerals. The proved reserves of seven kinds of minerals (coal, vanadium, molybdenum, lithium, etc.) are ranked in second positions respectively in the world. The proved reserves of five kinds of minerals (mercury, sulfur, phosphorus, etc.) are ranked in third positions respectively in the world. There is huge potential for further exploration of the above kinds of mineral resources in China[1]. However, the huge demands, the insufficiency of proved reserves, and the low level of utilization of mineral resources, the strong dependence on mineral resources of other countries, the prominent environmental problems caused by mineral exploitation, and the increased mines of resource-in-crisis have resulted in the severe situation of mineral resources in China.

1.1 Huge Demands for Mineral Resources

With the rapid industrialization and urbanization, China has entered into the middle stage of industrialization as the rapid growth of per capita consumption of mineral resources. Since 1990s, China's economy has developed at a dazzling speed. Its GDP is increased from 1.85 trillion RMB in 1990 to 30.07 trillion RMB in 2008. Corresponding to the high speed economic growth, the volume of consumption of major mineral resources is also increased rapidly (Fig. 1.1). From 1990 to 2006, the annual consumptions of aluminum, crude steel, and copper in China have increased about 12, 7.5, and 5.1 times, respectively (Table 1.1). Nevertheless, the per capita consumption (PCC) of most mineral resources in China is lower than that of the world average, much lower than that of the developed countries. Though China is the No.1 steel and copper consumer and No. 2 aluminum consumer in the world, the per capita consumptions of these metals are rather low. For example, the PCC of steel is only 88% of that of the world average, and is less than 20% of that of Japan. The PCC of copper is only 59% of that of the world average, and is less than 14% of that of the USA. In addition, the PCC of aluminum is only 67% of that of the world average, and is less than 13% of that of the USA[2]. Therefore, if the PCC of iron (steel), copper and aluminum in China in 2050 could reach the current level of those of the developed countries such as the USA and Japan, then the China's demands on mineral resources would become even much greater. Optimistically, China's demands on steel, copper and aluminum will increase continuously at a high-speed before 2025, and at a relatively steady growth speed then. It is expected that China's demands on steel, aluminum and copper will reach seven hundred million tons, fifteen million tons and seven million tons, respectively in 2025. They are 40%, 45% and 75% more than those numbers in 2008, respectively.

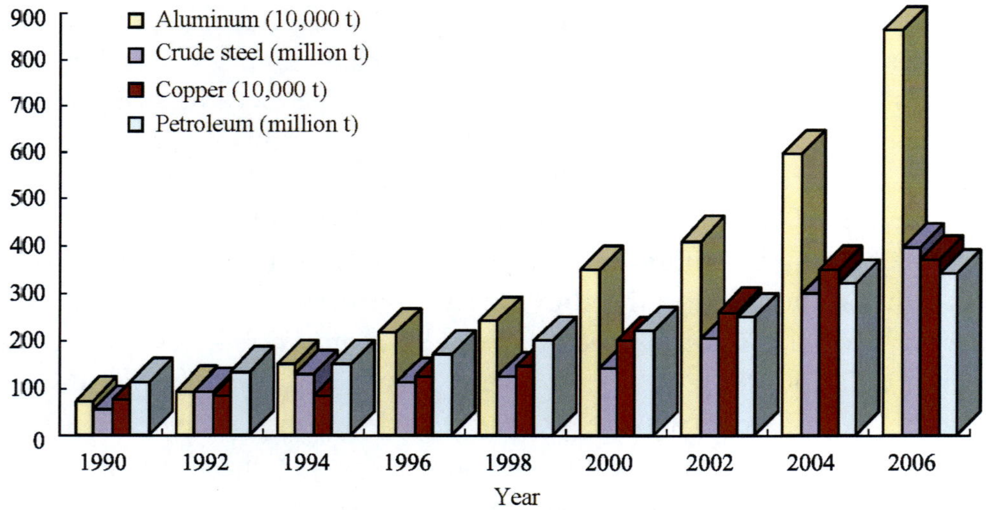

Fig. 1.1 The consumption growth trends of aluminum, crude steel, copper and petroleum in China between 1990 and 2006[3]

Table 1.1 Growth rate of China's consumption on aluminum, crude steel and copper from 1990 to 2006[3]

Year	Aluminum (10 thousand tons)	Crude steel (10 thousand tons)	Copper (10 thousand tons)
1990	72	5,300	73
2006	865	39,600	372
Growth rate (times)	12.0	7.5	5.1

1.2 Insufficiency of the Proved Reserves of Mineral Resources for Maintaining the Development of the Country

It is uncoordinated that the proved reserves of mineral resources, especially the major minerals in China, can not sufficiently meet the huge demands on mineral resources for the development of China. China has a large population. Its per capita proved reserves of mineral resources is only 58% of that of the world average, and is ranked in the 53rd position among countries in the world. The minerals with large reserves in China are mainly general ones. The reserves of strategic minerals such as iron, copper, aluminum and sylvite in China are seriously low. Their per capita proved reserves are about 35%, 17%, 11% and 5% of those average figures of the world[1], respectively. It is forecasted that the proved reserves of only 23 out of 45 kinds of important minerals in China will meet the demands of China's development in 2010, and only nine kinds of minerals will meet the demands in 2020 (Table 1.2). Moreover, the major minerals, such as iron, copper, aluminum, sylvite, manganese, chromium, precious metals and uranium, that are closely associated with the security of the state economy and people's livelihood, are in quite severe shortage situation at present. Recently, the gaps between supplies and demands of iron, copper, aluminum, manganese, chromium, nickel and sylvite in China are continuously increased. In 2007, the rate between imported parts and the total consumption of these minerals reached 52–97%[4, 5]. Since 1990, the trade deficit between the imported and exported minerals in China is getting bigger (Fig.1.2). In 2007, the deficit between the imported and exported minerals reached about US$100 billion, and the value of the imported minerals reached up to 31% of the total value of the imported goods[7, 8]. If this phenomenon is getting worse, the security of the state economy will be seriously affected. Therefore, the shortage of some mineral resources has become a crucial obstacle to China's socio-economic development and state security.

Table 1.2 Assurance degrees of the proved reserves of 45 kinds of major minerals comparing to the demands by the development of China in 2020[3]

Type	Number of minerals	Main minerals
Shortage minerals	5	Chromate, cobalt, platinum, sylvite and diamond
Cannot ensure	21	Iron, manganese, copper, plumbum, zinc, bauxite, stannum, gold, silver, strontium, fluorite, boron, barite, petroleum, uranium, nickel, antimony, refractory materials, sulphur, cement rock and kaolin
Basically ensure	10	Coal, titanium, tungsten, molybdenum, phosphorus, glass-making sand, masonry, gypse, kieselguhr and asbestos
Ensure	9	Natural gas, rare earths, magnesite, sodium salt, mirabilite, bentonite, graphite, talcum and wollastonite

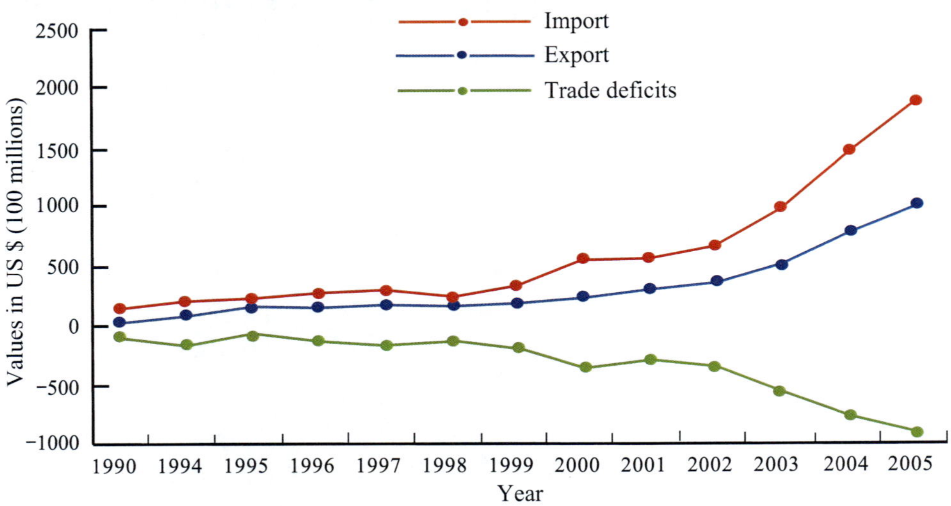

Fig. 1.2 A plot of values of imported and exported minerals and relevant deficits[6]

1.3 The Low Level Utilization of Mineral Resources and Prominent Environmental Challenges

The endowment of known deposits in China is relatively poor, with obvious following characteristics. ① Low-grade deposits are dominant in comparison with high-grade ones. The average grade of iron ore is only 33%. It is 20–30% lower than those of major iron ore suppliers in the world. The average grade of copper ore is only 0.87% which is about 1/3 of those of major copper producers. The average grade of manganese ores is only 22% which is about half of the industry standard grade of commercial manganese ores. In addition, most bauxite of China is composed of diaspore rather than gibbsite and boehmite[1, 3]. ② Small and medium-sized deposits are dominant in comparison with large and super large-sized deposits. For example, more than nine hundred copper deposits have been found in China. However, only 3% of them are large and super large-sized copper deposits, 9% of them are medium-sized deposits, and 88% of them are small-sized ones[9]. ③ The symbiotic and associated deposits are dominant in comparison with simple ones. For example, 80% deposits in China contain symbiotic and associated elements. 87 out of 139 kinds of elements were partly or wholly exploited and utilized from symbiotic or associated deposits[9]. The features of mineral endowment together with some reasons from management and science & technology resulted in many severe problems in utilization of mineral resources in China. One key problem is low level utilization of minerals. The total recovery of mineral resources and the rate of comprehensive utilization for symbiotic and associated minerals in China are only 30% and 35% (in average), respectively. They are 20% lower than those of advanced countries[10]. Furthermore, mineral resources have been seriously wasted. Another is great environmental disruption caused by mining industry. A large volume of waste residues (the total stock of tailings or solid waste in China was over 22 billion tons at the end of 2006[10]), waste water and waste gas caused by mining activities haven't been efficiently utilized and properly treated. They resulted in severe environmental pollution. Therefore, a large improvement should be made in utilization of mineral resources in China.

1.4 The Increased Numbers of Crisis Mines

Since the foundation of the People's Republic of China, great developments have been achieved in the mining industry in 60 years' efforts, and a relatively perfect exploitation system has been established. At present, there are over 500 large-sized mining enterprises and nearly 1,400 medium-sized mining enterprises. Nevertheless, a large number of large and medium-sized mines in China have to face challenge of mineral resource crisis after many years of mining. For example, at the end of 20th century, about 50% of 415 large and medium-sized mines encountered the problems of resource shortage. The consumed reserves of about half of 45 major kinds of minerals are more than the increased reserves by exploration. Based on these, Premier Jiabao Wen pointed out that the current urgent task is to seek new alternative resources in crisis-stricken (reserve shortage) mines. This will produce both social and economic benefit for China.

1.5 Huge Potential for Prospecting More Mineral Resources

It is believed that there are huge prospecting potentials for most kinds of minerals in China, except rich-iron ore, chromium, platinum metals, diamond and sylvite. This is supported by some following evidences. ① The distribution of three major metallogenic provinces (Circum-Pacific Metallogenic Province, Paleo-Asia Metallogenic Province and Himalaya-Tethys Metallogenic Province) in China indicates that there are favorable metallogenic conditions in China; ② Although more than 200 thousand mineral occurrences (deposits) have been found in China, only a few (only twenty thousand) of them have been properly explored and evaluated, most of them should be further properly studied, evaluated or explored, and a large number of geophysical and geochemical anomalies should be checked and verified[3]; ③ The low extent of geological investigation and mineral exploration in western China gives possible huge potential prospecting mineral resources whether in near surface or in deep earth; ④ There is good potential for prospecting minerals in many areas covered by vegetation and red soil in eastern China; ⑤ The depth of mineral exploration and exploitation in some countries is extended down to 2,500–4,000m in depth. However, the average depth of mineral exploration in China is less than 500m. This means that there is good potential for prospecting mineral resources underneath or near around the known orebodies of mines[11]. Accordingly, we thus believe that it is possible to find a large number of new deposits and to prove much more reserves of mineral resources in deeper places underneath covered areas and current mines in China if more effort could be put into detailed investigation and proper exploration of mineral resources.

2 A Roadmap for Scientific & Technological Development of Solid Mineral Resources in China to 2050

2.1 Overview of a Roadmap for Scientific & Technological Development of Solid Mineral Resources in China to 2050

Based on the above discussions, it is obviously shown that there are two basic and real contradictions related to the development of mineral resources in China. One is between the great demands on mineral resources and the severe shortage of the proved mineral reserves. The other is among the huge potential for prospecting mineral resources, the low level of utilization of mineral resources, the prominent environmental problems caused by exploitation of mineral resources, and the relative low extent of research, exploration and development of deposits. Then, how to make the huge potential to resources or reserves of minerals and to improve the efficiency of utilization of mineral resources are key questions should be solved in order to relax the tension of severe shortage of the proved reserves of mineral resources in China and to guarantee the coordinated development between exploitation and utilization of mineral resources and construction of ecological environment. In our view, we not only should be able to rationally utilize international mineral resources, to reduce the unit volume of minerals consumed for unit output, and to improve the mining management level, but also should put more effort to resolve three key scientific questions related to metallogenic theories and regularities, including the accumulation process of huge bulk metallogenic materials, the regularity of temporal and spatial distribution of deposits and the relationship between the metallogenic model and the relevant prospecting model, to specially make breakthroughs in three technological aspects, including the techniques for prospecting mineral resources in covered area and in depth, for cleanly and efficiently utilize mineral resources, for substituting and recycling mineral resources, and to strengthen the integration, test and application of relevant technologies, on the basis of systematically understanding the unique evolution history of the lithosphere in China (Fig. 2.1).

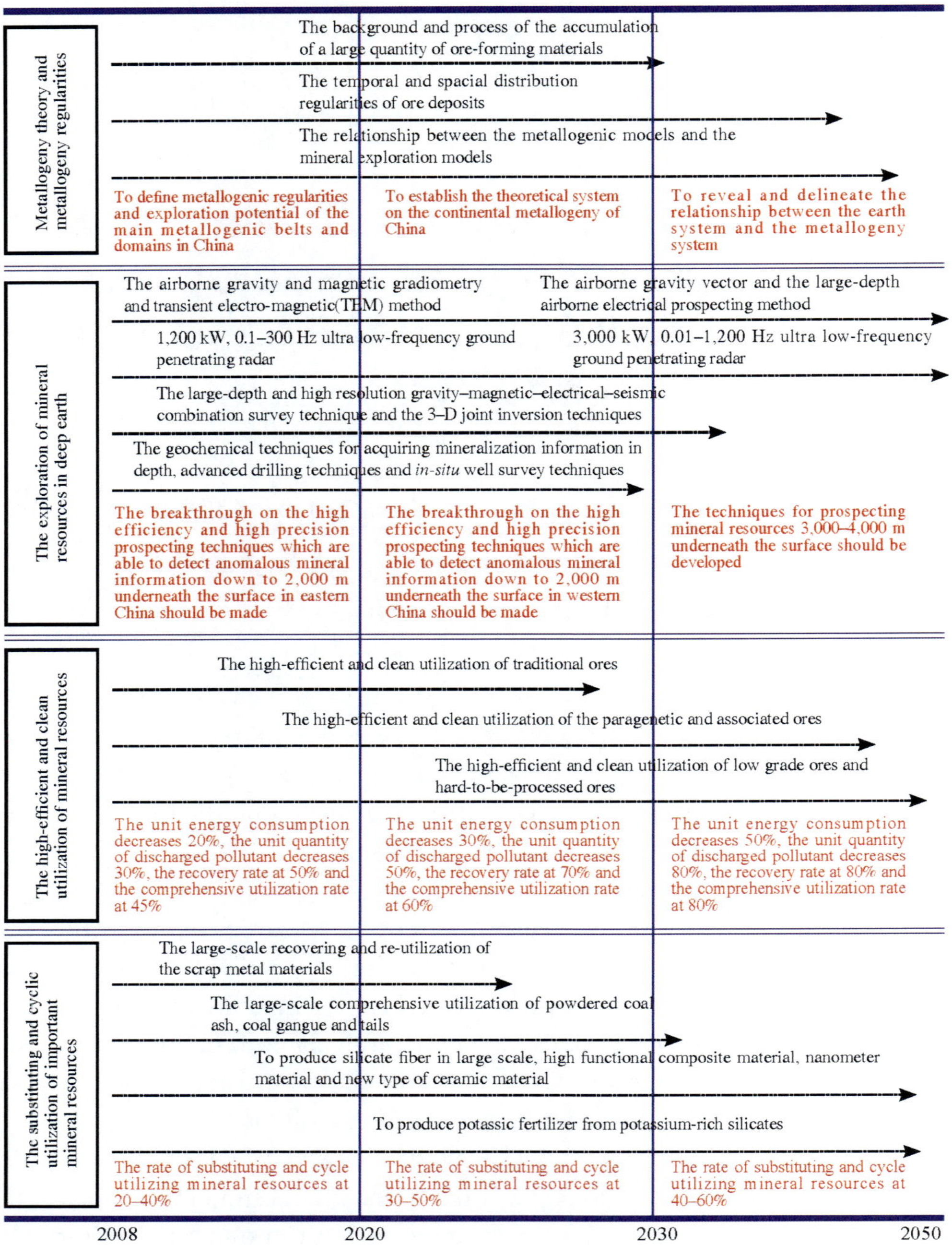

Fig.2.1 A roadmap for scientific and technological development of solid mineral resources in China to 2050

The recent, intermediate and long terms strategic blueprints (Fig.2.1) are given below. From present to 2020, our task is to make clear understanding of the metallogenic regularities and to determine prospecting prospects in major metallogenic regions and belts, to make breakthroughs on the precise testing techniques of element on site, aerogeophysical techniques, high-precision techniques for extracting metallogenic information and high-resolution geophysical techniques for detecting anomalies in depth (~2,000m) in eastern China, to improve the recovery of mineral resources in processes of mining, processing, and smelting and the rate of comprehensive utilization of associated elements in major mines, to carry out pilot studies on the alternatives for minerals with shortage of reserves (resources), to make breakthroughs on techniques for high efficiency recycling and utilizing used and wasted metal, and to actively improve the ecological environments of mines in China. From 2020 to 2030, our task is to set up the metallogenic theoretical system of the continent in China, to make breakthroughs on high efficiency and high-precision techniques for exploring targets in depth (~2,000m) in western China, on techniques for cleanly and efficiently utilizing low-grade ores and tailings, and on techniques for making fertilizer by using non-water-soluble potassium resources; to basically restore the ecological environment of historical abandoned mines, and to basically control environmental pollutions. From 2030 to 2050, our task is to reveal the relationship between the Earth system and the metallogenic system, to make breakthroughs on techniques for prospecting mineral resources in depth (3,000–4,000m), to develop a series of core techniques for cleanly and efficiently utilizing mineral resources, to make breakthroughs on techniques for replacing the major metallic materials by ceramic fiber, and to establish a sustainable system for the supply and utilization of mineral resources in order to guarantee the coordinated development between the exploitation and utilization of mineral resources and the construction of ecological environment in China.

The following main parameters should be reached. At the end of 2020, the rate of proved reserves and the resources within 2,000m beneath the eastern and central China should reach to 50%. The total recovery of mineral resources should reach to 50%. The rate of comprehensive utilization of mineral resources should reach to 45%. The energy consumption for unit production should reduce by 20%. The discharges of "three wastes" for unit production should drop down by 30%. The ecological environment of 45% of total abandoned mines should be restored, and the environment of 30% polluted areas of mines should be rehabilitated. Land reclamation rate in newly-built mines should fulfill 100%. The rate between alternative and recycled resources and the total consumed major mineral resources should range from 20% to 40%. From 2020 to 2030, the rate of proved reserves and the resources within 2000m beneath the western China should reach to 50%. The total recovery of mineral resources should reach to 70%. The rate of comprehensive utilization of mineral resources should reach to 60%. The energy consumption for unit production should reduce by 30%. The discharges of "three wastes" should drop down by 50%. The ecological environment of 65% of abandoned mines should be restored, and the environment of 50% polluted areas of mines should be rehabilitated. The rate between alternative and recycled resources and the total consumed mineral resources should range from 30% to 50%. From 2030 to 2050, the rate of proved reserves and the resources in depth of 3,000–4,000m should reach to 70%. The total recovery of mineral resources should reach to 80%. The rate of comprehensive utilization of mineral resources should reach to 80%. The energy consumption for unit production should reduce by 50%. The discharges of "three wastes" should drop down by 80%. The damage and pollution on ecological environment caused by mining, processing and smelting of ores should be basically controlled. The rate between alternative and recycled resources and the total consumed major mineral resources should range from 40% to 60%.

2.2 Metallogenic Theories and Regularities

2.2.1 Status-quo and Development Trends

(1) An Important Development Direction-studies on the Relationship between Continental Dynamics and Mineralization

Deposits are special geologic bodies in which certain elements were highly concentrated, in the evolutionary process of the Earth. Therefore, we must follow geoscientific regularities to study deposits. Macroscopically, we should start from many dynamical processes, such as global tectonic framework, evolutionary history of regional tectonics and local structural characteristics to study deposits. Microscopically, we should start from elements scale to study the geochemical properties of elements and chemical processes controlling the mineralization.

Since 1970s, the plate tectonic theory which was established mainly based on the study of the oceanic crust (Fig. 2.2) has resulted in a revolution in geoscience, especially, resulted in the promoted substantial progress of the researches on dynamics of the oceanic crust and the interaction between ocean and continent. However, like other geohypothesis, there are obvious some shortcomings in the plate tectonic theory for dealing with questions concerning the formation and evolution of continents except palaeozoic ocean-continent transitions, as only the horizontal movement rather than the vertical movement, the mantle convection rather than interactions of various layers of the Earth, and the plate margin rather than the plate interior were emphasized in the theory. Consequently, to study and discuss the characteristics and genetic mechanism of the geological activities of non-Wilson plate-tectonic cycle in continental interior becomes a great challenge and opportunity for geologists at present[12-17]. For this reason, USA made the 30-year-long (1990–2020) "Continental Dynamics Research Plan", which is expected to solve the limitations of plate tectonic theory for continents, to supple, improve and develop the plate tectonic theory, and finally to establish the continental dynamic theoretical system.

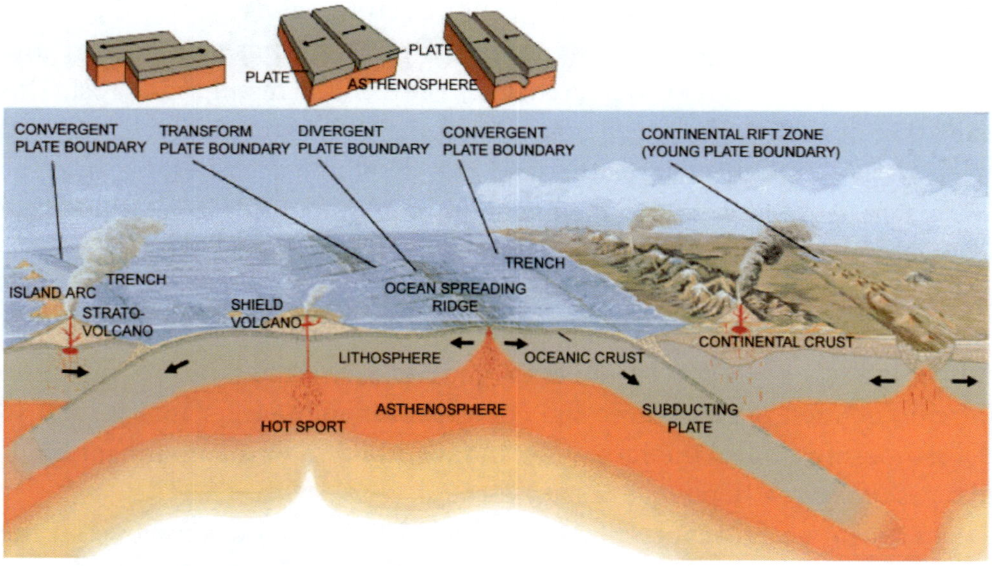

Fig. 2.2 A sketch map of plate tectonics (http://pubs.usgs.gov/publications/text/Vigil.html)

The appearance of plate tectonics resulted in an important advance in metallogenic theories, the profound transform on understanding of plate margin metallogenic system and mechanism[18, 19].Though the plate tectonics provides the theoretical framework for explaining the mineralization related to the evolution process of palaeozoic continental plate margins, it fails to explain the mineralization associated with the evolution of continental interior after plate collisions. Especially, there is no proper answer on the power source of metallogenesis and the genetic relationship among various types of mineral deposits. In this context, study on the relationship between continental dynamics and mineralization has become the frontier of geosciences, and has been widely regarded by geologists in the world. Based on a brief review of researches on the relationship between continental dynamics and metallogenesis in recent years, some development trends can be proposed as below.

1) In terms of metallogenic mechanism, the researches on metallogenesis and the interaction among various layers of the Earth are combined closely

At the turn of centuries, the proposal and wide discussion of the Earth system science profoundly affected various original disciplines of geosciences. At present, in order to create new generation knowledge system of geosciences for resolving the problems associated with resources, environment and disaster, most efforts are put on major pilot and innovative researches on one core frontier regarding the interactions among various layers of the Earth and three scientific themes including the lithosphere evolution, global changes, and deep process of the earth. The deposit is the product of the evolution of the Earth system. It is believed that the inevitable development direction of the ore geology, which is mainly concentrated on studies of the metallogenic process and environment, is to be put into the complicated Earth science system.

The interaction among different layers, especially between the crust and mantle, is one of core research subjects of continental dynamics. Based on the previous studies, there are extensive and various kinds of substance and energy exchange forms (two-way exchange) between the mantle and crust. This means that not only substances from partial melting of the mantle could add into the crust through underplating and mantle plume activities, but also the crust materials could return to the mantle through the subduction at the plate convergent margins and the delamination at areas with thickened lithosphere. Consequently, the exchanges between the mantle and crust resulted in the continental accretion and the mantle heterogeneity[20]. In addition, the various kinds of interactions between the crust and mantle resulted in the migration and redistribution of substances and energy in different layers, and further to macroscopically control the formation and distribution of the dominant kinds and types of mineral deposits in a large area.

In recent years, scholars have conducted beneficial discussions on the relationship between the crust-mantle interaction and mineralization. It is suggested that the crust-mantle interaction should play a very important role in the formation of large and super large deposits and metallogenic provinces. Moreover, it is believed that the crust-mantle interaction is one of the key factors for inducing various kinds of geologic activities in the metallogenic system, and is a key factor for affecting the composition, special and temporal structure of the metallogenic system and its ordered combination of various types of deposits[21-26]. Therefore, it can be seen that under the guidance of the new geosciences theories including the Earth system and geodynamics, to discuss the ore-forming mechanisms in the view of the migration and exchange of substance and energy in the process of the interactions between different layers of the Earth, to clarify the special and temporal evolution regularities of metallogenesis based on the regularities of special and temporal evolution of the metallogenic and geological background which was controlled by the evolution of Earth system, and then to establish metallogenic and prospecting models for supervising the exploration of large and super large deposits and metallogenic provinces have become an important development trend for researches on metallogenic theories and regularities.

2) In terms of the metallogenetic epoch, the intrinsic connections between metallogenesis and major geological events have been highly concerned

The metallogenesis needs a driving force. A large number of studies indicate that many large-scale metallogenies are closely related to the global or regional key geological events. For example, there is acoupling relationship between the life explosion in Late Sinian-Early Cambrian and the formation of large scale phosphorites all over the world; the mineralization of traps is closely related to the mantle pluming events[26-28]; the formation of porphyry copper deposits is related to the magmatic activities derived from the plate subduction[29-31]; the large-scale copper and nickel deposits in Sudbury of Canada may be related to the meteorite impact[32, 33]; and the gold deposits widely distributed in Shandong Province may be related to the direction turning of the Pacific Plate subduction[34].

Major geological events include plate subduction or cracking, mantle plume activities, delamination of lithosphere and underplating of mantle-derived magma, lithosphere extension and large meteorite impacts, etc. Different geological events can result in different sedimentation, metamorphism, magmatic activities and hydrothermal recycling, then induce migration, fractionation and redistribution of elements in the crust and even between crust-mantle layers, and subsequently result in the local enrichment of some useful elements and the formation of deposits. Researches on deposits related to the plate subduction and mid-ocean ridge extension have not only been a hotspot for more than fifty years, but also become an "incubator" for the new metallogenic theories and a primary driving force for making breakthroughs on mineral prospecting. The discoveries and researches of the Cenozoic deposits, including the porphyry copper, in Qinghai-Tibet Plateau, together with the studies on the metallogenesis in the Qinling Orogenic Belt and the Central Asia Orogenic Belt are pushing forward the progress of the theories of metallogenesis in orogenic belts[35-39]. Researches on the origin, evolution, and sulfide segregation of the large-scale basaltic magma in the mantle plume have unraveled the myth of abnormal enrichment of copper, nickel and platinum group elements (PGE) in Nioril'sk in Russia. It is believed to be resulted from the continuous accumulation of sulfide melts in the magma channel. A right direction for the prospecting of large-scale Cu-Ni sulfide deposits has been pointed out by this hypothesis[40]. Furthermore, researches on the relationship between lithospheric delamination and underplating of mantle-derived magma and the large-scale granite magmatic activities and metallogenesis in eastern China, have opened a new chapter for researches of geology and mineral resources[41-46]. With the advancement of the high-precision dating technology, some accurate data of metallogenic age implies that the large-scale metallogenesis in certain metallogenic provinces or systems often occur in a very short time period with an "explosive" feature, and close special and temporal coupling relationship with major regional geological events[41-46]. Based on above discussions, to completely analyze these intrinsic correlations, to understand how major geological events result in the activation, migration, agglomeration and metallogenia, to accurately perceive the regional metallogenic regularities, and then to provide theoretical basis for mineral prospecting are important development directions for researches on deposit geology in the future.

3) In terms of the metallogenic provinces, the metallogenesis around the plate margins has been paid further attentions, the metallogenesis within plate has become a new hotspot of researches

A large number of studies have shown that metallogenesis is extraordinarily developed in the plate boundaries (Fig. 2.3); there are totally different characteristics of tectonic settings and dynamics between the extensional-divergent boundary and convergent-subducted boundary of plates with obvious respective specializations in their associated diagenesis and metallogenesis. For example, massive sulfide deposits are mainly formed along the extensional-divergent boundary (mid-ocean ridge)[48-49], whereas porphyry Cu-Au deposits, epithermal Cu-Au deposits, orogenic gold deposits and other deposits related to granitic magma activities are mainly formed in the convergent boundary (subduction plate margin and orogenic belt)[25, 36, 37, 47, 50-52]. Therefore, the plate tectonics theory has no doubt pushed forward the development of deposit geology theories and the transform of mineral prospecting models.

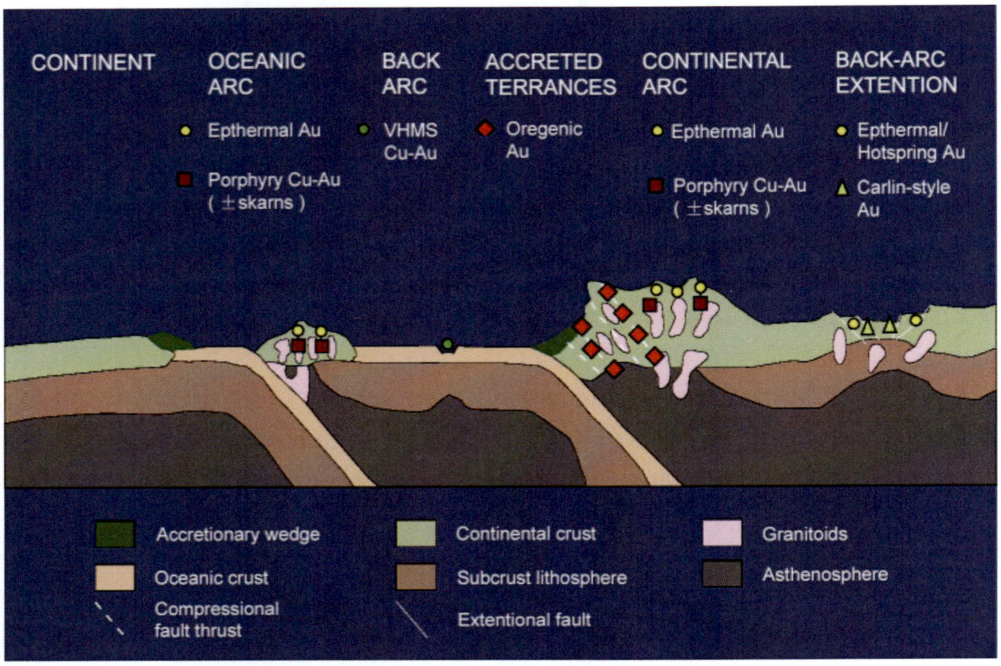

Fig. 2.3 The relationship between the main types of gold deposits and plate convergence-subduction boundaries [47]

In recent one decade, it is gradually recognized that the intracontinental geological processes, including large-scale lithospheric extension, lithospheric delamination, underplating of mantle-derived magma and mantle plume activities, after the plate collisional orogeny have important significance to the intracontinental metallogenesis. However, it is still a weak field of the researches on the metallogenesis occurred in the continental plate margins including the collisional orogenic belts, and the metallogenesis occurred within continental plate. Thus, to strengthen the above researches will greatly develop and enrich the theoretical system of relationship between continental dynamics and metallogenesis.

4) The space domain of observation and research is gradually expanded, and the interrelations among high-level metallogenic factors have been examined to explore the metallogenic regularities

At present, the researches on metallogenic theories and regularities are paid attention not only on single deposit, but also on the regional, continental and global scales. The research of global metallogenesis has gained initial results. It is expected to quest continuously the metallogenic regularities on the basis of the correlation among high-level metallogenetic factors. In general, the research in this area is still at the stage of description and data accumulation. Nevertheless, the study on the Earth system will surely inject new vigor and vitality to the study of metallogenesis. In addition, the profound investigation of the global metallogenesis will definitely give positive and crucial contributions for revealing the substantive relationships between the Earth systems and various metallogenic systems.

(2) The Application of New Technology and Methods and the Researches on Metallogenic Process and Models have been Paid Attention

1) With the increasing of disciplines intersection, the introduction of new technology and methods have been gradually more concerned

With the advancement of science and profound researches on metallogenesis, in order to explain complicated metallogenic phenomena, new demands on disciplines intersection are required by the researches on metallogenesis. The present study on metallogenesis has adapted many new disciplines, such as chemical thermodynamics, chemical kinetics, physical chemistry and computational science, besides other geosciences' sub-disciplines. In the meantime, the introduction of new technology and methods has been paid much more attention by researchers. For example, the establishment and improvement of analytical method of laser ablation inductively coupled plasma mass spectrometry (LA-ICP-MS) has promoted the researches on ore-forming fluids from roughly determination of fluid compositions by the measurement of bulk composition of fluids in multi-stage inclusions, to accurate determination of ore-forming fluids by direct measuring the composition of fluid in single inclusions[53-54]. The improvement of high resolution analytical and testing technologies of unconventional isotopes, such as Re-Os, Lu-Hf, Cu, Fe and Zn, has explored a new field for isotopic dating and tracing researches[55-57]. Moreover, the in-situ micro analysis of light isotope ratios by secondary ions mass spectrometry (SIMS) has become an important technical method for studying the ore-forming fluids[58]. All of these have provided new and important opportunities for producing output of key innovative achievements in the field of metallogeny.

2) More attentions have been given to study the detailed metallogenic process based on the researches on the original and final states of metallogenesis

Due to the restriction of the development of science and technology, the previous conventional researches of metallogenesis are only focused on the original and final states of metallogenesis, with limited researches on the metallogenic process and driving force. In recent years, the advancement of nonlinear science and experimental simulation technology, and further the improvement of analytical and testing conditions have made the study of metallogenic process possible. Major developments and trends in this field are given below. ① The experimental means are applied to study the physicochemical conditions of element activation, migration and precipitation in various kinds of geologic processes, on the basis of the combination between simulation experiments and thermodynamics and computational geochemistry, in order to quantitatively express various kinds of metallogenic geochemical processes[59-60]; ② The nonlinear science and chemical kinetics theories are incorporated into the researches on metallogenic process in order to quantitatively express the structural features of the metallogenic system and mechanism and velocity of various chemical reactions related to the metallogenesis[61-62]; ③ The advancement of microanalysis and testing technology has made it possible for the in-situ determination of elements and isotopic compositions in minerals at different stages in entire metallogenic process. This provides the prerequisite for understanding the composition of ore-forming fluids and features of different evolution stages of the metallogenic process in detail, as well as the conditions for depicting metallogenic process and establishing a more reasonable metallogenic model[54, 58]. Therefore, to understand the metallogenic process in detail by applying various new theories and methods has become one of the major development trends for metallogeny.

3) The study on metallogenic models is tended to change from single deposit model to regional metallogenic model

Metallogenic model is a highly rational generalization of metallogenic environment, process, source material and the distribution geometrics and regularities of deposits, and is one of the vital scientific issues, which have been researched for a long time in the metallogeny. The metallogenic models for porphyry copper deposits[63], massive sulfide deposits[64], and Carlin-type gold deposits[65] have served as an important impetus for prospecting relevant mineral resources all over the world. However, at present, the researches on metallogenic models are tended to be regionalized and multi-parameterized rather than limited to the portraying of typical deposits. To establish metallogenic models at scales of metallogenic province or belt[66-70], based on the researches on regional tectonic evolution and metallogenic series, has become a new hotspot for the research of metallogenesis. At the same time, to establish prospecting models in different scales, based on the multi-information from geology, geochemistry, geophysics, and remote sensing has also been widely concerned. Overall, more practical metallogenic and prospecting models based on the further studies will surely be better to bridge the relationship between metallogenic and prospecting theories, and then to establish a solid foundation for predictive prospecting.

China lies in the conjunctions of three major metallogenic domains (Circum-Pacific Metallogenic domain, Tethys Metallogenic domain and Palaeozoic Asian Metallogenic domain) (Fig. 2.4). China has favorable metallogenic conditions, and its various metallogenic systems and metallogenesis (such as large-scale low-temperature metallogenic system, large granite province metallogenic system, mantle plume metallogenic system, and large-scale metallogenesis of tungsten, antimony, rare earths) are unique in the world[68, 71]. The systematic researches on theories and regularities of metallogenesis in Chinese continent have great significance for prospecting mineral resources in China and for developing global metallogenic theories.

Fig. 2.4 The sketch showing the distribution of three major metallogenic domains in China

It should be pointed out that the Chinese continent is assembled by many blocks, with a complicated history of geological and tectonic evolution. Especially, the multiple collisions and fragmentation of several continents in Phanerozoic resulted in various smaller blocks, complicated framework of orogenic belts, and relative unstable craton, then resulted in the diversity and complexity of metallogenesis which are obviously different from those of other countries. Accordingly, in order to instruct the mineral prospecting and exploration in China, we have to clearly understand the metallogenic regularities and to establish suitable system of metallogenic theories and prospecting techniques on the basis of understanding and restoring the geological evolutionary history of tectonic domains and metallogenic provinces. According to the development trend of science and technology in the world, major existing problems, geologic characteristics of Chinese continent, and demands on mineral resources, we have sketched out a roadmap for the development of researches on metallogenic theories and regularities (Fig. 2.5).

2.2.2 Overall Objective and the Objectives in Different Stages to 2050

(1) Overall Objective to 2050

The overall objective is to study geodynamics, the crust-mantle interaction and associated mineralization, major geological events and associated mineralization, coupling mechanism of the metallogenesis and structure, fluid, substance, energy and chemical reactions, the special and temporal structure of various types of deposits and effective prospecting criteria of major the continent of China, and minor overseas, oceans and polars, to analyze and analogically study metallogeny at the scales of metallogenic province, large-scale metallogenic zone and various types of deposits, respectively, then mainly to solve major scientific issues such as the unique lithospheric evolution history in China, the accumulation process of huge massive metallogenic materials, temporal and spatial distribution regularities of deposits and the relationship between metallogenic and prospecting models, to establish a complete theory system of the metallogeny, and finally to provide a solid foundation for predictive prospecting of mineral resources.

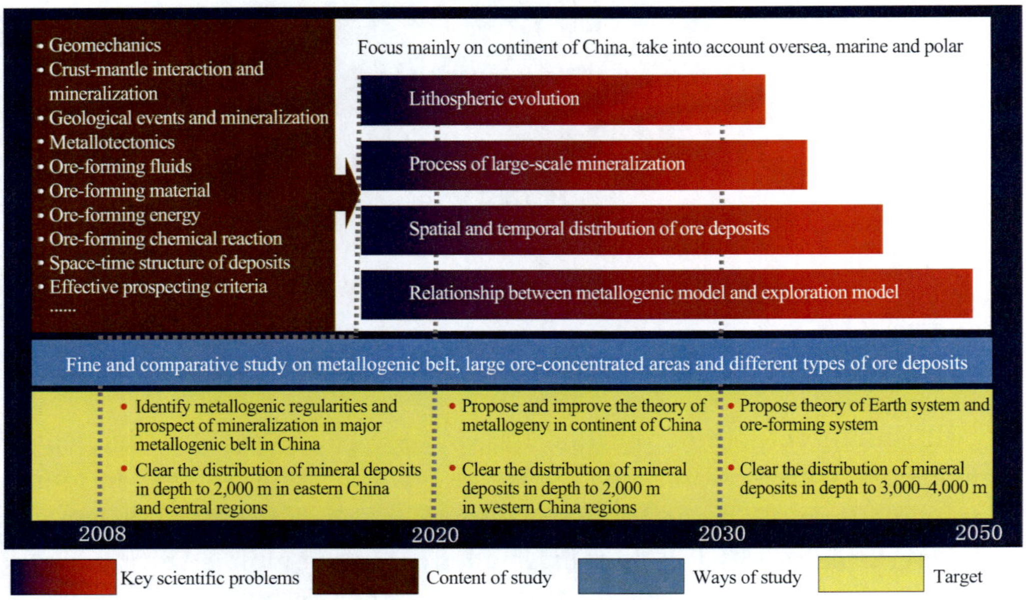

Fig. 2.5 A roadmap for scientific and technological development of researches on metallogenic theories and regularities

(2) The Objectives in Different Stages

By 2020, the metallogenic regularities and potential prospecting targets in major metallogenic provinces in China should be determined; the distribution regularities of major deposits in depth (within 2,000m) in eastern and central China should be defined. By 2030, the metallogenic theories of the continent in China should have established and improved, and the distribution regularities of major deposits in depth (< 2,000m) in western China should be defined. By 2050, the theoretical system of the Earth system and metallogenic systems should be established and the distribution regularities of major deposits in depth ranging from 3,000m to 4,000m in China should be understood.

2.2.3 Major Scientific Questions Should be Solved for Realizing the Objectives

(1) Temporal and Spatial Distribution Regularities of Deposits

The temporal and spatial distributions of deposits in the crust are heterogeneous. In terms of space, for example, the proved reserves of tungsten in China occupy more than 60% of those of the world, and the proved reserves of antimony exceed 70% of those of the world. The proved reserves of rare earth elements in the Bayan Obo super-large deposit, Inner Mongolia, are over 60% of those of the world. The proved reserves of gold (over 40,000 tons) in the Witwatersrand Basin in South Africa, which is only about 40,000 square kilometers, occupy 40–45% of the gold reserves in the world. The proved reserves of copper in several large-scale porphyry copper belts in central Chine (more than 300 million tons) possess about 35–40% of the global copper reserves. In terms of time, the proved reserves of banded iron formations, which are only distributed in Precambrian strata, possess about 60–70% of the global iron reserves. This heterogeneity is not clearly understood yet. It has been considered that this question is related to the evolution of the Earth. Therefore, to solve this question requires understanding the Earth system and the relationship between the Earth system and the metallogenic system. The main questions include the metallogenic dynamics of plate margins and intraplate, the heterogeneity of earth, the interaction of different layers in the Earth and its relationship to the heterogeneity of spatial and temporal distribution of deposits, the relationship between major geological events and metallogenesis, and the relationship between the environmental evolution of the Earth and the metallogenesis.

(2) The Accumulation Process of Massive Metallogenic Materials

Why massive metallogenic metals are accumulated in a very small space? And why certain elements are only accumulated here while other elements are accumulated there? These questions are not well resolved yet. In order to understand the metallogenic models of various kinds of deposits and their relationships, some following main questions should be solved. They include the driving mechanisms of various types of metallogenesis, types and characteristics of source suitable for the accumulation of massive metallogenic materials, the coupling mechanism of substance-energy-structure-chemical reactions for the accumulation of massive metallogenic materials, and the main controlling factors for the accumulation of massive metallogenic materials.

(3) Relationship between Metallogenic Models and Prospecting Models

The purpose of the research on metallogenic model is not only to understand the nature, but also to guide prospecting of mineral resources. There are cases for successfully guiding the mineral prospecting by applying metallogenic models. However, the metallogenic models only can be applied to confine a relatively large area for prospecting. In order to further reduce the area of the prospecting target and to improve the prospecting efficiency, we should find the relationships between the metallogenic and prospecting models. This means that the effective prospecting criteria should be determined on the basis of metallogenic models. Main issues include the tectonic settings of various types of deposits, styles of ore-controlling structure, rock association characteristics, strata association characteristics, mineral association and zonation, alteration association and zonation, element association and zonation and the four dimensional structure for deposits positioning.

2.2.4 Major Technical Ways to Attain the Objectives

(1) Systematic Researches on Three Major Metallogenic Provinces and Various Metallogenic Systems with Their Own Characteristics

Researches on major fundamental geological issues related to the important metallogenesis in China should be carried out based on the evolutionary characteristics of the continent in China. Main issues are given below.

1) The three-dimensional structure of the crust of three major metallogenic provinces and the metallogenic systems with their own characteristics in China should be drawn in detail and the coupling relationship between basin and mountain should be ascertained, on the basis of the comprehensive researches on geology, geophysics and geochemistry. In addition, the metallogenic process of the key regions should be depicted in detail, and the influences of structure and evolution of the lithosphere on the spatial and temporal distribution of major deposits in China should be explored.

2) The relationships between the temporal sequence of three major metallogenic provinces and the metallogenic systems with their own characteristics and the formation and evolution of the continent in China should be studied. The main metallogenic epoch of major types of deposits with various kinds of elements in China should be studied, and the influences of environmental evolution and major geological events on the metallogenesis should be explored.

3) Reworking metallogenesis should be paid attention. Based on the diversity and complexity of metallogenesis associated with fragmented continent and complicated frameworks of orogenic belts and mountain-basin, which were resulted from intensive movements of the crust in Phanerozoic, the mode, type and mechanism of reworking metallogenesis superimposed with various geologic movements, as well as the storage conditions of deposits should be studied and discussed.

(2) Analytical Researches on Large-scale Multi-metallogenic Provinces and Major Kinds of Mineral Deposits

1) Typical multi-metallogenic provinces and representative deposits should be selected for analytical research. The ages of mineralization and related geological bodies should be accurately determined by using high-resolution dating method in order to delineate the coupling relationship between metallogenesis and major geological events.

2) Geological and geochemical mapping in typical multi-metallogenic provinces should be conducted, combining with researches of petrology, ore-controlling structure, mathematical simulation and geophysics, in order to

determine the special structure of the large-scale multi-metallogenic provinces.

3) On the basis of the determination of geologic characteristics of metallogenesis, systematic studies on geological fluid, isotopic and elemental geochemical tracing should be conduct in order to determine the origins of ore-forming fluids/melts and to discuss the coupling mechanism of substance-energy-structure-chemical reaction for massive metallogenic materials accumulation.

4) The study on metallogenic process should be incorporated into the general framework of researches on geodynamic evolution. Through studying the structure and dynamic process in deep Earth, and discussing the mechanisms of the exchange of substance and energy , substance migration, and the fractionation, adjustment and accumulation of metallogenic elements in Earth's interior, the coupling relationship between the texture, structure and dynamics of deep media and metallogenesis should be established, and then the characteristics of vertical distribution and evolution of large, super-large deposits and large-scale regional metallogenesis should be unraveled.

Through above practices, the process, mechanism, and main controlling factors of the formation and migration of metallogenic fluids (magma), and the accumulation of massive metallogenic materials should be unraveled. The spatial and temporal distribution regularities of major deposits should be delineated. The metallogenic models in varied scales should be established in order to guide the optimization of prospecting targets and predicting concealed deposits in depth.

(3) Undertaking Researches on Comparative Metallogeny

There are prominent regional and temporal features in the metallogenesis. Therefore, it is very necessary to conduct researches on comparative metallogeny through international correlation programmes[72]. The issues for comparative studies are mainly listed below.

1) To carry out large space-scale comparative metallogeny, such as comparative studies on three major metallogenic provinces in the world, the metallogenesis in China and neighboring countries, and the metallogenesis in China and other countries supplying major mineral resources.

2) To carry out large time-scale comparative metallogeny, such as metallogenic characteristics in different periods, the reason of large scale mineralization in certain periods for certain elements, and the selectivity of metallogenic epoch for certain types of deposits, etc.

3) To carry out comparative studies on similar types deposits or similar multi-metallogenic provinces, such as the comparative studies on porphyry copper, MVT, VMS, SEDEX and IOCG types, the selectivity of metallogenic types for super large deposits, and so on.

4) To carry out comparative studies on the metallogenesis along plate margins and within plate, such as metallogenic dynamics and major deposits types, etc.

5) To carry out comparative studies on the metallogenesis of various

elements, such as the relationship between metallogenesis of metallogenic elements with different features and the Earth's evolution (Earth's environments), the metallogenic specialties of different types geologic processes or geologic bodies, etc.

Based on the above work, the relationship between major geological events and the Earth's evolution and metallogenesis should be unraveled. The metallogenic mechanisms and the possible deposit types in orogenic belts, other plate margins and within plate should be determined.

(4) To Extract Effective Information for Prospecting Resources According to Metallogenic Models

Based on the previous studies on the metallogenic environment and mechanism of major types of deposit in main metallogenic provinces or belts in China, combining with the available research results of comparative metallogeny, to improve and develop the metallogenic models of important deposits and to establish new metallogenic models. Furthermore, to extract prospecting models,based on the metallogenic models, to clarify ore-controlling tectonic styles, rock association characteristics, mineral association zonation, element association zonation, rock alteration zonation, distribution characteristics of diffused elements, characteristics of oxidizing zone on earth's surface, metallogenic physico chemical interfaces and four-dimension structural characteristics of deposits, etc. and then to make a bridge between metallogenic and prospecting models.

2.3 Predictive Prospecting and Minerals Exploration

2.3.1 Status-quo and Development Trend

(1) Transformation from Empirical to Theoretical and Technological Prospecting

The mineral prospecting has gone through a transformation from empirical to theoretical and technological prospecting. The theoretical and technological prospecting is to explore mineral resources by using proper advanced exploration technologies based on identifying how and where deposits were formed under the guidance of geoscientific theories. There are three stages for theoretical and technological prospecting. The first stage is in 1960s and 1970s. Some prospecting models were proposed based on studies of known deposits and then were applied to search for similar mineral deposits. In the second stage, the plate tectonics theory was applied to deal with metallogenesis around the plate margins and then to serve for prospecting minerals in the tectonic settings of plate margins. Since 1990s, the researches on the metallogenesis in the intra continent constrained by the continental dynamics process have provided scientific support for searching and prospecting mineral deposits formed in the continent during its evolution[73]. On one hand, the innovation of researches on metallogenic theories could give new ideas and orientations for further prospecting. On the other hand, the appraisal and prospecting of mineral resources are dependent on the innovation of exploration technologies. In a sense, the exploration technology is a bond between metallogenic theories and prospecting appraisal. Breakthroughs in mineral prospecting could only be made through correct understanding of metallogenic regularities and experimental studies on prospecting technologies and methods in different provinces under the guidance of metallogenic theories.

(2) Predictive Prospecting in Covered Areas and Very Deep Areas

As more and more prospecting work has been carried out, the chance for finding deposits on surface and in shallow depth is much less. At present, more exploration effort has been put on to find concealed deposits in depth rather than deposits on surface and in shallow level. Therefore, the exploration of resources in depth and under the coverage, which is known as "prospecting in depth for concealed deposits", has become the new orientation of predictive prospecting.

Theoretically, the most suitable ore-forming space in the Earth interiors is a zone, in depth of 5–10km beneath the surface, in which intensive exchange of substances and energy in the curst occurred and its associated dynamic activities converged, the metallogenic factors changed rapidly and experienced coupling transition, the metallogenic elements are suitable for accumulating and a lot of deposits are formed under internal and external dynamic activities. Comprehensive studies on some metallogenic belts have shown that the vertical extension of a large-scale hydrothermal metallogenic system can reach up to 10km.The 12km deep kola super borehole in Russia intersected the palaeozoic continental crust. The Cu-Ni, Cu-Zn, and Fe-Ti-Au mineralization are discovered at various depths, with the deepest Fe-Ti-Au mineralization intersected at 10km in depth[11].However, it is very difficult to prospect concealed deposits in depth comparing to prospect deposits on surface and in shallow level. Hence, it is more required than ever to make innovations in prospecting prognosis theories and advanced prospecting technologies.

(3) Geophysical Survey Technology

The geophysical survey technology becomes one of the major means of exploration for resources in deep areas due to the intrinsic penetrability of geophysical fields, including the underground electric field, magnetic field, seismic wave field and gravity field (Fig. 2.6). Though the working principles of most kinds of geophysical survey have been known gradually in 1970s, the qualitative leap forward in terms of accuracy, resolution, sensitivity, probing depth, interference free performance, mobility, automaticity and real-time on-site testing has only been achieved due to the considerable advances of modern manufacturing technology, electronic technology, computing technology, material technology, information technology, and space technology. For example, magnetic sensor is the core technology of the magnetometer. With the advancement of magnetic sensor, magnetometer was developed from the fluxgate type with sensitivity of only 1nT, to the nuclear proton type with sensitivity of 0.1nT, and now to the optical pump type with sensitivity of 0.01nT. Not only the sensitivity, but also the interference-free performance, mobility and automaticity of the new generation of magnetometer are highly improved. It is much easier to be operated and is more practical in the field. In addition, the MEMS digital grade geophone for seismic prospecting and the high-temperature super-conductive low-frequency magnetic sensor for electromagnetic prospecting could promote the development of geophysical survey to a new height. The wireless sensing network technology has provided great conveniences for the on-site gathering of geophysical data in the field.

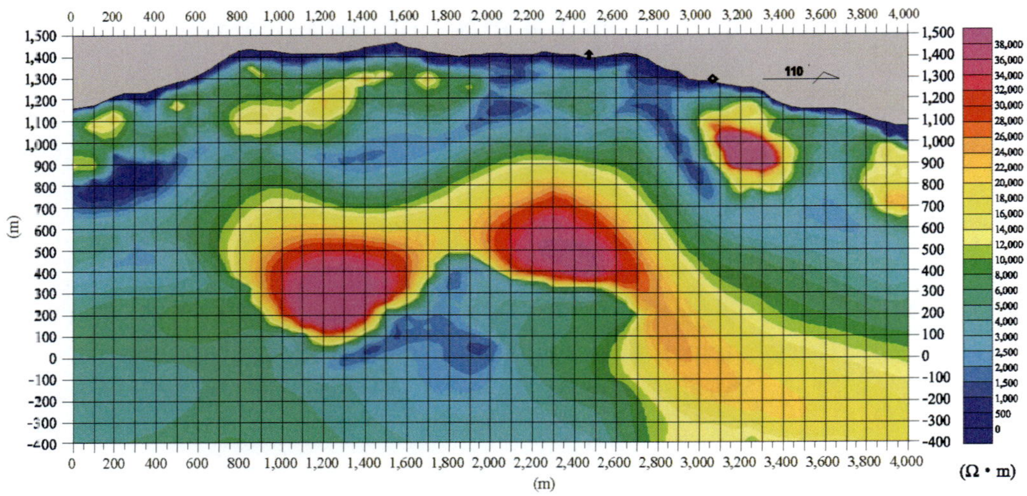

Fig. 2.6 A continuous bathymetric imaging section of the molybdenum deposits in Yechangping, Henan Province, in which the red is interpreted as porphyry, the molybdenum deposits are discovered beyond the porphyry (from J.M. Liu et al., unpublished data)

In the meantime, the technology portfolio of cross proving and cross complementing has replaced single technology. At present, there are various kinds of devices and methods in exploration geophysics and exploration geochemistry both at home and abroad, but there are some differences among deep probing technologies developed from different sub-discipline fields in terms of probing targets and environmental compatibility. Therefore, a suitable probing technology portfolio should be developed to meet the requirement of given environment and expected certain exploration targets. The integration of modern probing technology and development of technology portfolio suitable for the relevant metallogenic provinces are of vital importance to improve the hit ratio of exploration of concealed deposits and the work efficiency. Especially, It is so important for the exploration in China, as there are complicated geologic and metallogenic conditions and complicated landform, landscape and environment.

Therefore, the gravity, magnetic and electric exploration technologies are developing into two orientations in recent years. One orientation is to high precision, high resolution and three-dimension. Another is to the integration of gravity, magnetic and electric methods. There are not only close relationships but also differences between two orientations. The gravity, magnetic and electric survey methods could not play effective role in their integrated application for prospecting mineral resources until each of them has been developed to a certain extent. It can be seen that the first orientation is the basis of the second one and the second orientation is the objective of the first one. The integration at the current stage of development is not in general sense of simply putting things together, such as putting all relevant gravity, magnetic and electric data together for comparative study or simple cross-reference in order to find out their similarities, but, is to carry out multi-data joint inversion based on the explanations of data collected through various kinds of exploration methods. This multi-data joint inversion should be constrained by the seismic data and borehole survey and logging data, thus, it is a very promising method for integrated exploration.

Since 2000, a large advancement has been made in the large area strategic airborne geophysical prospecting technology. Especially, the aeromagnetic gradient, aerial gravity gradient and time domain aviation electromagnetic technologies are advanced remarkably. It is of far-reaching significance to the airborne geophysical prospecting in the future[74]. In recent years, with the improvement of sensitivity of magnetometer, particularly the magnetic compensation technology and positioning accuracy of airplanes, the quality of aeromagnetic gradient data is improved dramatically, and the quantity of the aeromagnetic gradient data is rapidly increased. Meantime, with the advancement of GPS technology, the accuracy of airborne gravity measurement is improved remarkably.

(4) Geochemical Exploration Technology

Over the past twenty years, geochemical exploration technologies were developed rapidly. The "International Geochemical Mapping Program" and "International Geochemical Reference Program" were designed and carried out in order to discover the places where large-scale metals are concentrated and then to serve for finding world-class deposits. How to obtain directly the ore-bearing information in large covered areas has been a headache problem for exploration geochemists for a long time. In view of the above difficulty, the international mineral circles have been devoted to develop or improve a series of geochemical prospecting methods with capability for detecting geochemical signals and collecting geochemical information in much deeper places. These geochemical methods mainly include the Geo-gas, geoelectrochemical method (CHIM), element organic matters association form method (MPF), enzyme extraction method (Enzyme leach), mobile metal ion method (MMI), etc. In recent years, the "Deep Penetration Geochemical Method Correlation Program"[75] was organized by the International Exploration Geochemists Association for the purpose of improving various kinds of geochemical methods in order to serving for prospecting large and super large concealed deposits. The latest advancements of researches include that the concept of deep-penetration geochemistry has been set forth. The deep-penetration geochemical methods for prospecting concealed multi-metallogenic provinces or super large deposits have been developed. In addition, the three-dimensional dispersion model for elements in the supergenic environment has been established based on researches on landscapes of strongly weathered crust. This provides a solid foundation for searching concealed deposits in regions of thick weathering crust[76]. Generally, the trends of development of geochemical exploration technologies include the transition from the prospecting theories based on the metallogenic environment to those based on the accumulation of large-scale metals; the transition from the study of surface information to the study of transportation process of the deep metallogenic information and their redispersion or enrichment mechanism after they were transported to the surface, and the transition from discovery of local anomaly to the discovery of large-scale anomaly caused by large and super large deposits.

(5) High-precision Exploration Remote Sensing Technology

Over the past ten years, with the rapid development of the space technology and computer technology, and the application of quantitative remote sensing anomaly into regional prospecting prognosis and potential appraisal of mineral resources, our mankind have opened a new era for prospecting mineral resources by using remote sensing. The exploration and prognosis of metal deposits by using multi-spectra and high-spectra (ETM^+, Aster, Aviris, etc.) data were paid attention in the world. There are successful application cases in Europe, Asia, North America, South America and Australia[77].These methods were mainly used for prospecting porphyry copper deposit, and partly were used for prospecting polymetallic ore deposits such as lead, zinc and precious metal deposits. The remote sensing technology is mainly applied for prospecting mineral resources in the gobi, desert and areas of exposed bedrock in the world, with relative good effectiveness of application. Especially, the spectral resolution of high-spectra remote sensing is better than 1% of the wavelength, reaching the nanometer (nm) level, and its number of spectra channels reaches up to tens or even hundreds. Its combination of spectral information of ground objects, which were determined by substance composition, with the space images, which reflect the existence pattern of ground objects, has imparted each pixel of the space image with the characteristic spectral information. Thus, this is named imaging spectra technique. The combination of remote sensing images and spectra has united the logical and imaginable thinking in the epistemology, has greatly enhanced people's cognitional ability of the objective world, and provided an effective means for people to observe the ground objects and perceive the world.

At present, the newly released Aster data, which were collected by 14 spectral channels from the visible light to thermal infrared, are expected to have a good application prospects. Because there are five channels of wave bands in near infrared zone in the Aster rather than one channel of the seventh wave band in the ETM+ and another five channels of wave bands in the thermal-infrared zone in the Aster rather than one channel of the sixth wave band in the ETM+, the capability of the Aster for identifying various kinds of minerals and rocks is much greater than that of the ETM+. At present, the Aster data and associated technologies have been applying to conduct survey and appraisal of potential mineral resources in the covered area in some countries. The development of new techniques of remote sensing for exploration and appraisal of potential mineral resources in the covered areas under the guidance of metallogenic theories in combination with the GIS platform-based multiple information integration technology are expected to contribute to making important breakthroughs in prospecting and appraisal of mineral resources.

(6) Quantitative and Intelligence-based Development of Techniques for the Deposit Location Prognosis

The combination of computer technology and new exploration technology is one of the important development orientations of techniques for mineral prospecting. The rapid development of modern computer technology has not only greatly improved the capability of data acquisition and computation of the modern geophysical devices, but also provided a platform of comprehensive operation and systematic analysis for integration of data collected from various kinds of exploration techniques, airborne survey data and geologic data. The platform provides a unified visualized digital framework for sorting out, analyzing, cross-verifying and vector superposing relatively isolated data of various fields that were unable to be integrated, then for obtaining multidimensional constraints for the prospective objects and for establishing automated multivariate data fitting system and visualized interpretive analytical model. With the development of the computer technology and application of GIS, the capability for recognizing weak information has been improved greatly. This provides the precondition for the quantitative and intelligence-based development of the prospecting target prognosis and deposits positioning.

(7) Comprehensive Survey Technology

The replacement of single technology by the association of cross-verifying and complementary technologies represents the general orientation of the development of mineral prospecting prognosis and exploration[78]. At present, there are many kinds of geologic, geophysical, geochemical and remote sensing methods for mineral prospecting. However, there are some differences among these various kinds of exploration technologies in terms of the probing targets and the suitable application environment. Therefore, to meet requirement of the given environment and expected certain exploration targets, a suitable association of probing technologies for relevant mineral exploration is needed. The integration of modern probing technologies and the development of regionally appropriate technology association are very important for improving the rate of finding concealed deposits and work efficiency.

In 1999, the International Concealed Deposits Exploration Workshop was held in Sydney. The achievements of application of new technologies and techniques into the discovery of concealed deposits are exhibited. This has prompted Australia to initiate its huge "Glass Earth" program[79], which is designed to make a "transparent" underground within 1,000m in depth in Australia by using geologic, geochemical and geophysical exploration technologies in order to find next generation giant deposits in Australia. Lately, Canada has also proposed a program similar to the "Glass Earth", attempting to make a "transparent" underground within 3,000m in depth in Canada in order to find the next generation giant deposits in Canada. The Australia's "Glass Earth" program is focused on three themes which are to build capability of obtaining new data, to build capability of discriminating, integrating and interpreting new data, and to build prospecting model suitable for the continent of Australia.

A wide range of projects are currently under implementation in the "Glass Earth" program. They mainly include developing new generation probing technology, to understand geologic processes of regolith and underlying bedrock, to advance geographic information technology, to develop conceptual model of deposits discovery and predictive model of topography. Its main technical issues (Fig. 2.7) include the airborne gravity gradient measurement, airborne geomagnetic tension gradient measurement, airborne electromagnetic measurement, airborne and satellite mineral geochemical mapping, undergroundwater geochemistry, isotope geochemistry and surface geochemistry, the coupling simulation of chemical flow, fluid flow and heat flow in rocks and surficial soil, the visualized data integration and transformation technology, and the new drilling technology.

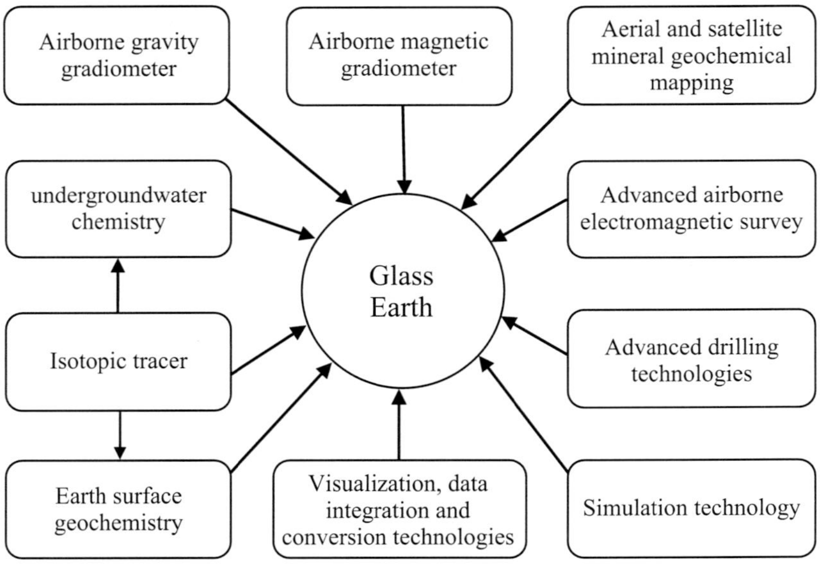

Fig. 2.7 Major technologies and methods in Australia's "Glass Earth" program[79]

As a new exploration notion, the "Glass Earth" Initiative has many merits to be learned.

There are widely covered areas (vegetation and soil coverage area, desert and gobi area, rock coverage area, etc.) in China. How do we prospect mineral resources in these covered areas? On the other hand, the depth of exploration and mining in some major mining countries reached from 2,500m to 4,000m. Some Cu, Zn, Fe,Ti and Au mineralization zones have been intersected about 6km below the surface in the Kola super borehole of Russia. However, the depths of exploration and mining in China are relatively shallow, mostly less than 500m (Fig. 2.8). There are two reasons why they are much shallower than the average of those for similar deposits abroad. One is that we have neglected researches on metallogenic theories and prognosis for metallogenesis in depth for a long time. The other is that we are lacking of technology and method for pinpointing the concealed deposits in depth. More details are given below ① The geology and structures of continent of China are relatively complicated. There are many metallogenic types and diversified metallogenic environments. These resulted in difficulty to establish models for prospecting mineral resources in depth. ② Scientists and engineers in China are less experienced in prospecting mineral resources in depth. The probing capability and combined effect of geophysical fields are not well given, and the geologic, geophysical, geochemical data have not been closely integrated for serving the mineral prospecting in depth. In addition, there are few successful cases for reference and no systematic assembly results. ③ There is lack of integrated, effective, pertinent technology and methods association for prospecting mineral resources in very deep places. ④ There is lack of data processing softwares and nationalized instruments and devices with own intellectual property rights. ⑤ There is lack of geophysical technology platform and relevant infrastructures for prospecting metal deposits. Therefore, it is imperative to conduct researches on theories and technologies for exploring concealed deposits in deep places in order to increase a large amount of reserves of mineral resources in China.

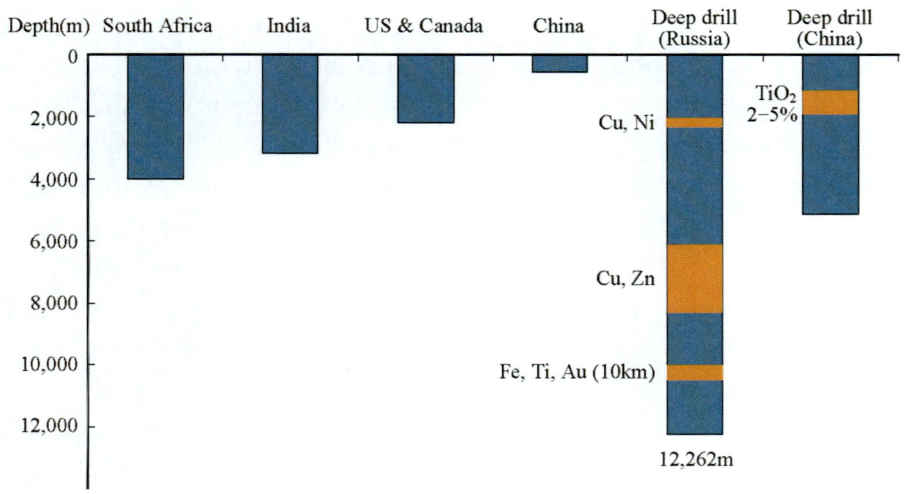

Fig. 2.8 Mining depth comparison between China and other countries [11]

Based on the development trend of science and technology in the world, the main existing problems, the status-quo of prospecting prognosis and mineral exploration in China and its demands for mineral resources, a roadmap of development for researches on prospecting prognosis and exploration of mineral resources has been sketched out (Fig.2.9).

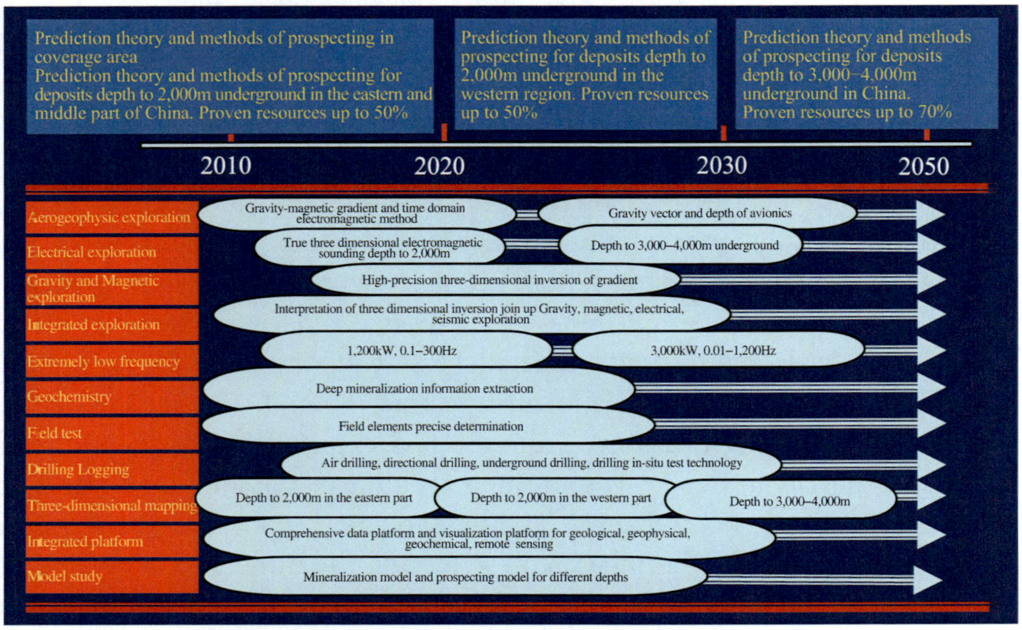

Fig. 2.9 A roadmap of scientific and technological development for mineral prospecting prognosis and exploration

2.3.2 Overall Objectives and Various Stage Objectives to 2050

(1) Overall Objectives to 2050

The overall objectives are to take the covered areas and the deep areas of existing mines as the subject of study under the guidance of achievements of researches on metallogenic theories and regularities, to comprehensively carry out innovations and applications of such probing technologies as airborne geophysical prospecting, ground electric survey, magnetic and gravity survey methods, and extremely low frequency electromagnetic (WEM) exploration technology, to improve technology for extracting information of mineralization in depth, to develop high precision technology for on-site determining element contents, to develop technologies of air drilling, directional drilling and underground drilling, and in-situ measurement technology of elements in borehole, to conduct three-dimensional geological and geochemical mapping, to establish integrated digital platform and visualized platform of geological, geophysical, geochemical and remote sensing data, to establish comprehensive systems of exploration theories, technologies and methods for prospecting mineral resources under the covered areas and the concealed deposits in deep places, then to provide theoretical and technological supports for precisely outlining mineral resources in covered areas and deep areas (500–4,000m in depth).

(2) Various Stage Objectives

From present to 2020, our stage objective is to establish theories and methods for prognosis prospecting mineral resources under the covered areas and in deep places within 2,000m in depth in the eastern and central China, with the rate between the proved reserves and resources within 2,000m in depth of 50%. From 2021 to 2030, our stage objective is to establish theories and methods for prognosis prospecting mineral resources within 2,000m in depth in the western China, with the rate between the proved reserves and resources within 2,000m in depth of 50%. From 2031 to 2050, our stage objective is to establish theories and methods for prognosis prospecting mineral resources within 3,000–4,000m in depth in China, with the rate between the proved reserves and resources within 3,000–4,000m in depth of 70%.

2.3.3 Major Scientific and Technological Issues to be Solved to Attain the Objectives

(1) Basic Issues Associated with the Metallogenic Prognosis of Concealed Deposits

1) Maximum theoretic depth of the formation of deposits and its controlling factors

This is to determine the ore-forming pressure and then to estimate the ore-forming depth, to evaluate the maximum theoretical depth of the formation of various types of deposits and the main controlling factors based on the pre-existing data both at home and abroad.

2) Palaeogeomorphological characteristics when deposits were formed and conditions for preservation of deposits

This is to determine the relationship between the characteristics of palaeogeomorphology when deposits were formed and those of present morphology, and to determine the states of reworking and preservation of deposits.

3) The regularities of vertical zonation and elements association and fractionation

This is to study the regularities of spatial distribution of deposits at the regional scale to study the spatial association and fractionation regularities of metallogenic elements at the deposit field scale, to study the metallogenic zonation of different metallogenic elements at deposit or ore body scale, especially to pay attention to the indicative function of vertical zoning on deep concealed mineralization (body) besides the horizontal zoning of elements.

4) Metallogenic models and regularities of deposits at different scales

This is to grasp the metallogenic regularities and to establish metallogenic models at different levels, based on detailed studies on metallogenic geological environment and metallogenic mechanism, in order to guide the optimization of prospecting targets and prognosis of concealed deposits.

(2) The Technology for Extracting Information of Mineralization in Depth from Near Surface Environment

1) Response of ground water to deep mineralization information

This is to extract information and geochemical "fingerprints" of bedrock and concealed deposits to sort out the most effective mineralization information for exploring deep concealed deposits, on the basis of the major elements, trace elements and isotopic compositions in the ground water.

2) The technology for extracting information of mineralization in depth from surface media

This is to study the element and isotopic compositions of geogas in the soil or of the soil itself, and then to extract the information of concealed mineralization in depth.

3) High-precision deep-penetration geochemical theories and methods

This is to improve precision and penetration capability of the strategic deep-penetration geochemical prognosis theories and methods, which were conventionally applied to other large landscape areas through experiments, then to apply them to the tactical prognosis of deep mineral resources.

4) On-site high-precision element testing technology in the field

This is to develop high-precision portable on-site elements testing instrument in order to improve the efficiency of on-site observation and research on deposits.

(3) Technologies and Methods for Probing Deposits in Depth

1) Airborne geophysical prospecting and remote sensing technologies for extracting mineralization information in covered areas

This is to develop the new airborne geophysical prospecting and remote sensing technology for probing mineral resources in the covered area, so as to provide information for appraisal of prospecting project in the covered area, especially to develop aerogravimetric gradiometer, light-duty high-precision multi-probe magnetic gradiometer and airborne transient electromagnetic observation system, and to develop high spectral and super-high spectral remote sensing technology.

2) Electromagnetic three-dimensional deep probing technologies and methods

It should be noticed that the in-depth research, development and application of the method with combined natural and artificial electromagnetic fields is very important. In addition, to develop new static correction method is also very important. At present, no static correction method is universally applicable to various conditions and regions. Obvious weaknesses are existed in the two-dimensional inversion-based curvilinear translation method, impedance tensor resolution method and spatial filtering method. It is predicted that the more reliable three-dimensional inversion-based static correction method could be developed.

3) Theories and methods for deep penetration capability of the frequency

spectrum induced polarization

The induced polarization (IP) is the most direct and effective geophysical method for prospecting base metal deposits. As limited by the potential field theory, the probing depth of the conventional DCIP method is usually less than 500m. Therefore, it is necessary to actively explore and develop the theory and method for applying frequency spectrum induced polarization of the inductive electromagnetic field for probing much deeper under large power situation. They include researches on forward modeling, inversion theory, calculation method and software programming.

4) Extra low frequency electromagnetic wave related theories and methods

The transmitter station of artificial source of extra low frequency electromagnetic wave is fixed, and the receiver stations are across the country, with distances ranging from hundreds to thousands of kilometers between the transmitter and receiver stations. This method utilizes the electromagnetic wave signals transmitted between the Earth surface and the ionosphere. Researches on the theories and methods of transmitting characteristics, signal processing, data inversion and data application of the extra low frequency electromagnetic wave are required.

5) The application of seismic methods in geophysical prospecting for metal deposits

In regions with complicated geological structures, in particular the metal mine fields, there are many difficulties for the seismic exploration. Therefore, it is necessary to conduct systematic researches on the elastic wave propagation theory in complicated media and on mathematical and physical simulations of various kinds of seismic waves on geologic and geophysical models. In addition, efforts should be put on methods, instruments, data acquisition, processing and interpretation so as to establish a probing and interpreting system for the effective seismic exploration of metal deposits.

6) The joint inversion of gravity, magnetic, electric and seismic methods

The joint inversion of gravity, magnetic, electric and seismic geophysical survey is an integrated geophysical interpretation method which is effective for solving complicated geological problems, and is a currently reliable and quantitative integrated geophysical interpretation technology. Currently, there are two basic models. One is the joint inversion based on unified geological and geophysical model, which is established to make connections between all methods based on the interconversion between parameters of physical properties. The intrinsic link between the integrated information and geological model can be used to complement and constrain each other so as to reduce the multiplicity of interpretations of the inversion. The other is a joint inversion based on unified mathematical, geological and geophysical model. This is to establish a mathematical and physical model for unifying various kinds of geophysical prospecting information, to carry out unified data processing and inversion imaging of geophysical prospecting information, to unify various mathematical physical models of multiple geophysical methods into one common mathematical physical model and then to carry out unified data processing and inversion imaging on the basis of the utilization of relationship between diffusion field and wave field through mathematical manipulation. Meantime, the non-linear joint inversion can applied to greatly promote the quantification of geophysical interpretation and to improve the objectiveness of the interpretation. It is also one of the development orientations in the future[80].

7) Three-dimensional forward and inversion and interpretation technologies

The gravity, magnetic and electric exploration methods actually belong to a physical field volume-based geophysical exploration method, with its intrinsic characteristics of the volume effect. The one-dimensional and two-dimensional inversion results are as in fact always approximate, whereas the three-dimensional inversion results are much better. For example, only the three-dimensional inversion method rather than the two-dimensional one could be adopted to obtain a correct inversion result for a petroleum and gas-bearing tectonic zone. Three-dimensional inversion has been applied to effectively improve the survey accuracy. In recent years, the stochastic subspaces inversion method has been initially applied to the gravity and magnetic explorations, but not to the electric exploration yet.

8) Air drilling, directional drilling, underground drilling and the in-situ measurement technologies of boreholes

It is required to actively develop the air drilling, directional drilling, underground drilling and the in-situ measurement technologies of boreholes for rapidly, efficiently and properly exploring deposits in depth.

(4) The Precise Positioning Model of Deposits in Depth

In order to evaluate prospecting target and to position the concealed deposits in depth, it is required to establish a method system for exploring and evaluating concealed deposits in depth and a visualized three-dimensional model for positioning deposits in depth, on the basis of the integrated prospecting information of geology, geophysics, geochemistry and remote sensing by the geographic information system (GIS).

2.3.4 Major Technical Means to Attain the Objectives

(1) To Conduct Comprehensive Technology Integration and Pilot Demonstration in Typical Metallogenic Districts

The see-through technology of tactical exploration in metallogenic districts, which is similar to the modern medical detection technology, is to invert the property and structure of the geologic body in depth by using data, which were detected on the surface, reflecting the electric, magnetic, seismic wave and geochemical fields, based on the researches of metallogenic theories and ore-forming regularities, in order to detect the spatial position, shape and size of the concealed mineralized geologic body through the covered area. The geophysical signals can either be natural or artificial. Usually, the artificial field signal, which is characterized with high intensity, high frequency and high resolution, mainly reflects the situation of shallow parts underneath the surface, whereas the natural field signal, which is characterized with low intensity, low frequency and poor resolution, can reflect the situation in deep areas[81].

The see-through technology of tactical exploration in metallogenic districts mainly consists of high-resolution electromagnetic mapping and depth-probing techniques, complemented by high precision magnetic survey, high precision gravity survey and high resolution seismic imaging techniques. The rapid geophysical mapping techniques, which are generally applied to investigate geologic bodies in depth of 0–150m, include IP, extra low frequency electromagnetic, high precision magnetic surveys, etc. The section profiling techniques, which are generally applied to investigate geologic bodies in depth of over 1,000m, mainly consists of continuous conductivity survey, induced polarization survey, source-controlled audio frequency electromagnetic survey, transient electromagnetic survey, and shallow seismic imaging technique, etc.

The gravity and magnetic surveys are very conventional geophysical prospecting techniques. In order to meet the requirements for deep exploration, these techniques should be improved in terms of precision and sensitivity of the surveying instruments (hardware ability), inversion software, and topographic correction, etc.

The reflection seismic technique is mainly used to detect the petroleum and natural gas resources in several kilometers depth. It is rarely used in the exploration of metal deposits due to its relatively low resolution reflecting geologic bodies in shallow levels and in steep pitch. However, with the improvement of data acquisition and innovation of inversion software in recent years, these two problems have been generally solved. As for metal deposits exploration, the reflection seismic method is mainly used to understand the fine structure and to discuss the possible tectonic position of deposits in depth with the help of other geophysical prospecting techniques and geological interpretations.

(2) Multi-disciplinary Three-dimensional-mapping in Major Metallogenic Provinces and Belts

With the reference of Australia's "Glass Earth" program, a multiple-disciplinary Three-dimensional-mapping in major metallogenic provinces and belts in China should be conducted by using geological, geophysical, geochemical and remote sensing techniques, with mapping depths of 1,000m, 2,000m and 3,000–4,000m respectively for different periods. The conduction of Three-dimensional-mapping has not only collected necessary data for deep deposits exploration, but also provided a good experimental opportunity for the improvement of the above-mentioned techniques.

(3) To Carry out "Extra Low Frequency Ground Probing Project"

The extra low frequency (WEM) ground probing project is characterized by its artificial emitted signals, which have strong immunity to interference, wide coverage, stable signals, large investigation depth and small measuring deviations. Through the measurement of orthogonal horizontally and vertically reciprocal observational network, the real three-dimensional data at all layers of a large area could be obtained ,the two-dimensional or three-dimensional geologic images and the high-precision underground electric property distribution patters could be obtained by a single run of computer processing, and then the distribution of mineral resources in depth could be evaluated. This technique has advantages which are unparalleled by others. As no transmitting devices are required on site during exploration, the exploration efficiency can be improved greatly, and the working intensity of field staffs and exploration costs in the field could be reduced greatly. Thus, it is very suitable for the complicated geological settings and landforms in China.

At the beginning, we will start the extra low frequency ground probing project with a gross power of 1,200kW and a frequency range of 0.1–300Hz. After 2020, we should be able to increase its gross power to 3,000kW, to extend its frequency to range of 0.01–1,200Hz, and to develop various kinds of its applications.

(4) To Build Multiple Information Integration Platform and Three-dimensional Visualization Platform

Data acquired by various kinds of technologies are needed to be calculated comprehensively and analyzed systematically on a unified platform in order to extract more useful information. The ever-changing database technology and GIS technology featured by spatial analysis in modern times have made it possible to build such a kind of platform. The platform provides a unified visualized digital framework for sorting out, analyzing, cross-verifying, and vectors superimposing data, which are hard to be integrated, of isolated survey, spatial and geologic surveys of various fields, thus to obtain multi-dimensional constraints for the prospecting targets and to establish automated multi-variate data simulating system and visualized interpretive analytical model.

Three-dimensional visualization is not only a means for displaying graphics but also for checking the extent of rationally understanding the data, such as all-inclusive dynamic interpretation of three-dimensional data. In order to expedite the three-dimensional visualization researches on non-seismic data, the seismic interpretation workstation could be directly utilized when the formats of gravity, magnetic and electric data have been converted into the format suitable for seismic workstation.

(5) Instrument Researches and Manufactures

Though the exploration geophysics research in China has its place in the world, and the equipments, instruments and interpretation methods are in state-of-the-art, almost all of large-scale geophysical prospecting equipments and instruments, high-precision geophysical prospecting instruments, and core processing and interpretation technology in China are imported. This results in a widen gap between China and the developed countries in terms of the independence and innovation ability of geophysical exploration.

It is suggested to set up a long-term special fund for the research and development of geoscientific instruments and experimental equipments, and to implement a systematic geophysics instruments development plan. This plan aims to greatly improve the geophysical prospecting instruments and equipments in terms of capability and function such as large power, deep penetration, high resolution, high precision, high ratio of signal-to-noise, anti-interference, multi-channel acquisition, multi-parameter, real-time monitoring, efficiency and speed, and automation, on the basis of the multi-channel separation type and synchronized array type real three-dimensional data acquisition and multi-component, multi-function (eg., the on-site measurement of physical properties and parameters of rocks and minerals, the simultaneous operation of electromagnetic frequency sounding and frequency spectral induced polarization) and multi-parameter data acquisition. It also aims to make more stable, reliable, small, and portable equipments with humanized, friendly interface and bundled software kit of international level.

Efforts should be put on the research and development of ground high resolution geophysical instrument with surveying capacity of 3,000m in depth and distributing type geophysical data acquisition system. Efforts should be put on the development of large power transmitting, electric three-dimensional survey data acquisition, data processing and inversion technologies, on the research and development of high precision gravimeter and gradiometer, on the research and development of high precision three-component magnetometer for surveying borehole and on the innovation of borehole and ground three-dimensional inversion and interpretation technologies. The geophysical prospecting instruments, which should be also researched and developed, for surveying borehole include large penetration distance electromagnetic wave and sound wave instruments, in-situ element measurement instruments, transient electromagnetic surveying instrument, etc.

In terms of airborne geophysical prospecting instrument, efforts should be put on the research and development of time domain fixed wing airborne electromagnetic instrument and on the discussion of data processing and interpretation method, with capability of investigating down to 300m in depth. In addition, the homemade airborne magnetic gradient survey instrument and gradiometer are urgently required to be developed.

It is noteworthy that geologic research, application of geophysical and geochemical technology and drilling and excavation are the three basic elements for prospecting mineral resources in depth. Geologic research is the basic condition, geophysical and geochemical exploration methods are the technological supporting condition, and the drilling and excavation in prospecting works are the practical condition. These constitute the basic technical line for prospecting mineral resources in depth. The research, experiment and development of the above technologies and methods cannot be done without the basis of geologic research and the support of prospecting work verification. Therefore, the research and development of air drilling, direction drilling and underground drilling equipments are also very important.

2.4 Clean and Efficient Utilization of Mineral Resources

2.4.1 Status-quo and Development Trend

The development trend of the clean and efficient utilization of mineral resources in the world is high recovery, low cost, energy- conservation, environment-friendly, healthy and safety. High recovery means to improve the utilization efficiency of mineral resources through technological innovation. Low cost means to reduce the cost of unit output. Energy conservation means to reduce energy consumption of unit output. Environmental-friendly means to reduce emission of noise, discharge of waste gas, waste water, dust and other chemical pollutants of unit output. Healthy and safety means to improve working safety of workers and to reduce chances of exposure to hazardous materials. With decades of efforts, China has obtained remarkable achievements in the utilization of mineral resources. Nevertheless, a lot of issues to be improved are mainly given below.

(1) The Inefficient Utilization of Mineral Resources

There are many problems in the utilization of mineral resources in China. The major challenge is low level of utilization of mineral resources. The average gross recoveries of mineral resources and average comprehensive utilization rates of paragenic and associated minerals are about 30% and 35% respectively, which are 20% lower than the advanced level in the world. The utilization rate of tailings is less than 10%. Mineral resources are severely wasted[10].

A distinct feature of deposits in China is that there are more paragenic and associated deposits and less single kind of deposits. About 80% of the deposits in China contain paragenic and associated elements, and 87 out of 139 kinds of minerals exploited and utilized are partly or wholly from paragenic and associated deposits, accounting for 63% of the total[9].Therefore, the comprehensive utilization of mineral resources is a very important task for China.

The high proportion of low grade and hard-dressing ores is another main feature of mineral resources in China. For example, the average grade of iron ore is only 33%, lower than the average level (50–65%) of main iron ore suppliers in the world by 20–30%, average grade of copper ore is only 0.87%, less than 1/3 of that (2–5%) of main copper producers, average grade of manganese ore is only 22%, less than half of the standard of industrial manganese ore, and the bauxite is mostly composed of diaspore, which are very difficult to be separated and extracted, with little gibbsite and boehmite [1, 3].

The exploitation and utilization of complicated multi-element paragenic ores, low-grade and hard-dressing ores is an important task for China. However, there is lack of technologies suitable for the comprehensive utilization of the above ores in China. Firstly, the manufacture of traditional minerals in China is characterized with features of complicated processing procedures, long time process and high cost. Secondly, the automatically controlling level for dressing and smelting ores is relatively low comparing with the advanced level abroad. Thirdly, researches on large, efficient and low-consumption dressing and smelting equipments are in low level. Fourthly, there is lack of advanced equipments for recycling of tailings, waste residues and other solid wastes. These problems have constrained the benefits of comprehensive utilization of deposits and the comprehensive utilization of low-grade, mixed and fine disseminated ores.

Primary products are still dominant for the metal ores dressing and smelting industry in China. For example, China is a large molybdenum producer with major outputs of molybdenum concentrate, molybdenum oxide and ferromolybdenum. A large amount of molybdenum products in poor quality are produced and exported by many small-sized enterprises. In terms of high level process of molybdenum including chemical engineering, molybdenum electrode and molybdenum crucible, the variety and quality of molybdenum products from China are much less and worse than those from the abroad. There are similar cases in terms of lead, zinc, tungsten, tin and other elements. The average level of equipment and technologies in China for processing non-metallic minerals including purification, ultrafine grinding, lump processing, tint processing and modification processing is much lower than that of the developed countries. It is common in China that primary mineral products are normally exported whereas fine processed mineral products need to be imported.

(2) The Discharge of a Large Amount of Waste Gas, Waste Water and Solid Waste and the Severe Pollution of the Ecological Environment

A large quantity of dust and toxic gases, discharged during ore dressing and smelting processes, is one of the main sources of air pollution in China. There are awful numbers of small township enterprises for ore dressing, coking, mercury smelting, zinc smelting, sulfur smelting, etc. in some poorly managed mining districts. The small scale operation and investment, shabby equipment and out-dated technology of those small township enterprises resulted in low rate of the resources utilization and large volumes of discharged waste gases. Statistics has shown that the extraction rate of sulfur in indigenous sulfur smelting method is lower than 30%. Over 60% sulfur is discharged into the atmosphere in forms of SO_2, SO_3 and H_2S . In Guizhou Province, a large amount of harmful elements such as mercury and cadmium has been discharged into the atmosphere in the indigenous zinc smelting process [82-83]. The indigenous mercury smelting process resulted in severe mercury pollution to the atmosphere and soil environments [84-85].

The mine wastewater includes the pit drainage during the construction and production of mines, the tailing water produced during ore washing by adding organic and inorganic agents, and waste water formed with rainwater and leached solvable substances from open pits, dumps, tailings and waste rock piles. The annual discharged waste water from ore processing in China is about 3.6 billion tons, with recycling rate of only 65–70%. Most of the waste water is discharged without any treatment. It resulted in direct or indirect pollution of the surface water, ground water and surrounding farmland, field and the crops. The volatilization of some harmful elements also resulted in air pollution.

Studies have shown that the tailings or solid wastes produced annually by mining in China, which are increasing gradually, and have reached to 1.7 billion tons annually. By the end of 2005, the total accumulated solid waste in China has reached to 22 billion tons. The acidic, alkalic, toxic, radioactive or heavy metal components, contained in the solid waste of the mining industry, could be decomposed easily by oxidation if the solid wastes have been stockpiled in the open space for a long time. These discharged toxic and hazardous materials would contaminate the water and soil, jeopardize the human health and affect the industrial and agricultural production. In 2003, the red mud discharged by the aluminum industry alone in China was 9 million tons, and the accumulated stock so far has reached 100 million tons. The red mud contains high concentration of alkalic materials and salts. The solid waste from the mining industry is also detrimental to the farmland by occupying and damaging it.

A part of raw mineral resources, which were left in the underground adit or waste rock piles, tailings and waste residue, and were not effectively utilized, has become the solid waste in the mining industry. In 2006, the productions of copper, lead, zinc and nickel in China are 760 thousand tons, 740 thousand tons, 2.14 million tons and 70 thousand tons, respectively. If the comprehensive recovery rate of non-ferrous metal ores is taken as 60%, the exploited copper, lead, zinc and nickel resources which were unable to be recovered for effective utilization in that year are 500 thousand tons, 490 thousand tons, 1.43 million tons and 50 thousand tons, respectively. The total amount of wasted resources in past years would be tremendous.

The waste water, waste residue and tailings discharged from processing and smelting are the main source of pollution to the ecological environment. Studies have shown that the wastes left from mercury ore smelting are the main pollution source in the mercury deposits area in Guizhou Province[86]. The rice grown in the region contains enriched toxic methyl mercury, which is a potential hazard to the health of local residents [87-88].

In general, the mining industry of China is characterized with low rate of utilization of mineral resources, high energy consumption, high index of waste discharging and severe environment pollution. To improve utilization efficiency of mineral resources and to follow a green path for mining industry are conspicuous problems to be urgently solved. In the meantime, they are also important for relaxing the contradiction between the supply and demand of resources in China.

It is noteworthy that in order to promote the development of recycling economy, to improve the utilization efficiency of resources, to protect and improve the environment and to promote the transformation of economic growth mode, "The Recycling Economy Promotion Law of the People's Republic of China", which was deliberated and enacted on August 29, 2008 by the Third Session of the Eleventh National People's Congress after three years' discussion and modification, was implemented on January 1, 2009 in China. A series of supporting regulations will be enacted to make the enforcement of the Law.

Therefore, it is important to solve problems effectively on the critical technology and equipment for the utilization of ores and solid waste, particularly the low grade ores, complicated paragenic ores, conventional ores, large and bulky tailings and waste residue, through technological innovation and integration, then to improve the utilization efficiency of mineral resources in China, to greatly reduce the discharged amount of "Three Wastes", and to promote the coordinated development between development of mineral industry and the environmental protection. A roadmap for the development of mineral resources is given in Fig.2.10. Main objectives at different stages are given in Table 2.1.

Table 2.1 Objectives for efficient utilization of mineral resources at different stages

	Presnt-2020	2020-2030	2030-2050
Indices for energy conservation and discharge reduction	The energy consumption is reduced by 20%, waste discharge is reduced by 30%, and to establish a single mining group mode	The energy consumption is reduced by 30%, waste discharge is reduced by 50%, and to establish a mining ecological park mode	The energy consumption is reduced by 50%, waste discharge is reduced by 80%, and to establish a social circulation mode
Utilization rate of paragenic and associated ores	50%	70%	80%
Comprehensive utilization rate	45%	60%	80%
Mineral recovery rate	50%	70%	80%
Water reclamation rate	70%	80%	90%
Tailing recycling rate	30%	50%	70%
Ecological environment restoration rate of historically abandoned mines	45%	65%	100%
Restoration rate of polluted environment	30%	50%	100%
Land rehabiltation rate of newly-built mines	100%	100%	100%
Comprehensive utilization level	Reach the current level of the developed countries	Catch up with the simultaneous level of developed countries	Catch up or exceed the advanced level of developed countries

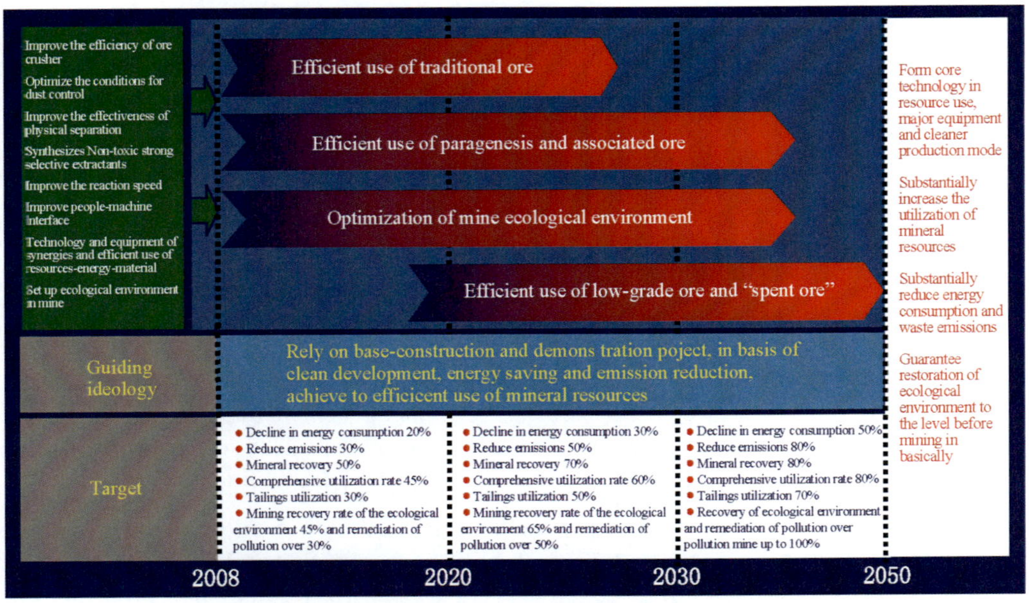

Fig. 2.10 A roadmap for scientific and technological development of the clean and efficient utilization of mineral resources

2.4.2 Overall Objective and Objectives at Different Stages to 2050

(1) Overall Objective to 2050

Taking the efficient utilization as the core of the overall objective, base construction and demonstration project as its priority, and the clean development and energy conservation & discharge reduction as its precondition, researches will be carried out on four kinds of subjects including the efficient utilization of conventional ores, the efficient utilization of paragenic and associated ores, the efficient utilization of low-grade ores that are unable to be utilized at present but will be able to be utilized in the future, and the optimization of ecological environment of mines. According to the characteristics of these four kinds of ores, through improving the ore crushing and grinding efficiency, optimizing the dust control conditions, improving the physical separation efficiency, strengthening the development of nonhazardous and nontoxic and strong selective extracting agents, improving reaction velocity and man-machine interface during ore dressing and smelting, strengthening the research and development of the technology and equipment for coordinated and high efficient utilization of resource-energy-materials and the building of ecological environment of mines, our overall objective is to form the core technology for utilizing mineral resources efficiently, to form clean mode of production by large equipments, and to greatly improve the mineral resources utilization rate, to greatly reduce the energy consumption and the amount of discharged wastes, in addition, to rehabilitate the polluted ecological environment of the mines and to restore the previous ecological environment before mining.

(2) Objectives at Different Stages

1) From present to 2020

The objective from present to 2020 is to reduce energy consumption per unit output by 20%, to reduce waste discharge per unit output by 30%, and to establish a single mining group mode in which the waste materials from the previous process of production will be properly treated and then to be used as the raw material or its substitution in the original process of production or in other processes of production.

50% of the total paragenic and associated deposits shall be comprehensively developed, with the comprehensive utilization rate of about 45%. The gross recovery rate of mineral resources shall reach 50%. Especially, the waste water utilization rate and the tailing utilization rate in processing plants shall be 70% and 30%, respectively, which is the present level of developed countries.

The ecological environment of mines shall be greatly improved. The restoration rate of ecological environment of the historically abandoned mines shall be 45%. The rehabilitation rate of polluted environment shall be over 30%. Land reclamation rate of newly-built mines shall be 100%. New exploitation projects that will have destructive, irretrievable influences on the ecological environment will not be approved. The treatment rate of "Three Wastes" in mines will reach the national standard. In newly-built mines, reclamation and mining shall be processed simultaneously. Laws and regulations on protection of environments in mines shall be improved, and check and supervision on prevention and control of ecological environment in mines shall be strengthened. Propaganda and education shall be strengthened to improve the awareness of mining ventures and the entire society on the conservation of resources and environment.

2) From 2020 to 2030

Comparing to the present level, the energy consumption per unit output shall be reduced by 30%, the amount of discharged waste per unit output shall be reduced by 50% and a mining ecological park mode shall be established. In the mining ecological park mode, some waste materials, energy and byproducts, which could not be recycled by a single mining enterprise itself, shall be able to be used as the raw materials or power by another or some other enterprises, through the inter-enterprise network, in which the flows of materials, energy and information are coordinately conducted.

70% of the total paragenic and associated deposits shall be comprehensively developed with the comprehensive utilization rate of about 60%. The gross recovery rate of mineral resources shall reach 70%. Especially, the waste water utilization rate and the tailing utilization rate in processing plants shall be 80% and 50%, respectively, which shall catch up the level of developed countries at that time.

The ecological environment of mines shall be further improved. The restoration rate of ecological environment of the historically abandoned mines shall reach 65%. The rehabilitation rate of polluted environment shall be over 50%.

3) From 2030 to 2050

Comparing to the present level, the energy consumption per unit output shall be reduced by 50%, the amount of discharged waste per unit output shall be reduced by 80%, and a social circulation mode shall be established. The mining circulation system, as a part of the entire social system, is connected with other sub-circulation systems of the entire social system, to promote the combination of circulation economy in various forms and scales, to improve the means of consumption and demand for mineral resources and to improve the utilization efficiency of mineral resources.

80% of the total paragenic and associated deposits shall be comprehensively developed, with the comprehensive utilization rate of about 80%. The gross recovery rate of mineral resources shall reach 80%. Especially, the waste water utilization rate and the tailing utilization rate in processing plants shall be 90% and 70%, respectively. Many indices shall reach or surpass those of the developed countries at that same time. The rehabilitation and restoration rate of ecological environments of the polluted mines shall be 100%.

2.4.3 Major Scientific and Technological Issues to be Solved to Attain the Objectives

(1) New Technologies on Efficient Mining, Processing and Smelting of Complicated Polymetallic Ores and on Those Process Intensification

The green exploitation technology, mining technologies that produce no or little waste and the in-situ solving and leaching ore technology should be developed to maximally reduce the volume of produced wastes. Researches on technologies for processing low-grade ores and for processing and smelting paragenic and associated ores in large-scale mines shall be undertaken. The short-procedure technology of direct leaching, purification and separation shall be coordinately combined with thermal decomposition process. The clean leaching system and the non-scrap separation purification system that discharge little waste shall be applied for processing. The multiphase reactor combined with the technologies of complex leaching and heterogeneous catalyst reaction will be applied to recycle the useful components in the ores, in order to meet the objective of short-procedure, high yielding, low discharge and low energy consumption. The critical scientific and technological issues to be resolved are given below.

1) Green exploitation technology that produces no or little wastes and the in-situ solution leaching and large-scale heap leaching technologies.

2) New methods for strengthening momentum transfer, mass transfer and heat transfer.

3) New types of biological and chemical catalytic reactions and catalysts.

4) Short-procedure chemical and biological metallurgy technology.

(2) Environment-friendly and Efficient Ore Processing Agent and Separating Media and Equipment

It is necessary to conduct the molecular design based on the mineral-agent surface interaction, and to develop new processing agents and large-scale equipments for specially processing and smelting the conventional hardly processed and smelted ores, paragenic and associated ores, low-grade ores, tailings, coal ashes and other wastes. It is also necessary to synthesize new kinds of non-toxic or less toxic ore dressing agents, to study automatic control technologies and green smelting technologies for processing plants in order to improve the resources recovery rate and to reduce the amount of discharged "Three Wastes", and then to reduce the amounts of produced and discharged solid waste, waste water and waste gas from the source.

In order to form efficient synthesis and separation extraction technologies, then to greatly increase the added-value of products, researches on how to develop large-scale fluidized calcine equipment should be conducted, the gas metallurgical technology that is able to extract metals directly from complex minerals should be actively developed, the normal temperature normal pressure hydroformylation reactor and high temperature high pressure hydroformylation reactor should be studied and developed. With the integration of the present existed extraction metallurgy technologies and newly developed technologies, a new way of energy conservation and resource conservation utilization of mineral resources should be established. Their automation level should be improve. The energy consumption and cost per unit output should be reduced. The exposure of workers to hazardous materials should be reduced and the discharge of "Three Wastes" per unit output should be decreased. The critical scientific and technological issues to be resolved are listed below.

1) Syntheses of efficient and strong selective extracting agent.

2) Syntheses of non-toxic and pollution-free processing agents and development of biological processing agents.

3) The coordinated and efficient utilization technology and equipment platform for resources-energy-materials.

(3) "Three Wastes" Treatment and Ecology Restoration Technologies

The cycling utilization technology of ore processing waste water (including tailings reservoir overflow water) should be developed. High efficient processing procedure and technology for treating heavy metal-bearing ore dressing waste water should be studied. Researches on how to recycle and reutilize the waste gas from smelters should be carried out. The technology for comprehensive utilization of solid waste from ore processing, such as the technologies for re-processing of tailings and for recovering peragenic and associated minerals and valuable elements should be developed. The technologies for using tailings to make building materials and for using tailings and waste rocks to fill the mined-out area and slump settlement should be developed.

Technologies and methods for ecological restoration and reconstruction in mines should be studied and developed. New breakthroughs in critical technologies for green exploitation with surface conservation, detection, evaluation and treatment of the foundation of mined-out areas and building theoretical system for monitoring and evaluating environmental safety of the reclaimed and rehabilitated mine areas should be made. Relevant demonstration projects should be established and undertaken.

It is necessary to develop the combined biological, physical and chemical technology for rehabilitating and restoring heavy metal polluted soils, to develop critical technology for safe treatment, disposal and reutilization of wastes by plant rehabilitation, to develop the integrated technology for restoring and rehabilitating the heavy metals polluted soils, to develop technology for immobilized degradation of organic matters in mine areas by microbes, to develop biological surfactant intensified restoration technology, the in-situ microorganism rehabilitation technology, the combined plant-microbial rehabilitation technology, and the technology for controlling and rehabilitating radionuclide contaminated soils. The critical scientific and technological issues to be resolved are given below.

1) Mineral microbe project and mineral new material technology.

2) Technology for effectively treating organic and heavy metal pollution and water environment technology.

3) Mines safety engineering technology.

4) Soil restoration, monitoring and evaluation.

2.4.4 Major Technical Means to Attain the Objectives

The status-quo of mineral resources utilization in China results in that the modernized improvement of traditional techniques and the wide application of new technologies are the orientation of future development of the utilization of mineral resources. For example, China is relatively rich in gold ores which are hard to be processed at present with resources of about 1,000 tons, accounting for one-fourth of the proved reserves of gold deposits. The gold state and mineral composition of ores are the main basic reason caused difficulty of treatment. According to analysis of characteristics of process mineralogy, the gold ores that are difficult to be processed can be divided into three categories.

First type is the gold ore with high contents of arsenic, carbon and sulfur. It generally contains over 3% arsenic, 1–2% carbon and 5–6% sulfur. The gold leaching rate of this type of ores treated by the conventional cyaniding method is only about 20–50%, with huge consumption of Na_2CN. When the floatation method is adopted, relatively high grade gold concentrate can be obtained. However, the high concentrations of arsenic, carbon, antimony and other harmful elements in gold concentrate will adversely affect the further gold extraction process.

Second type is the ore in which gold is existed in forms of very fine and micron particles in the gangue minerals and harmful impurities. It contains about 1–2% sulfides. About 20–30% of gold particles are distributed in the lattices of gangue minerals. Whether the conventional cyaniding method or the flotation method is applied to process this type of ore, the gold recovery rate is very low.

Third type is the ore in which gold is closely associated with arsenic and sulfur. Its characteristics are that arsenic- and sulfur-bearing minerals are the main carriers of gold, and they contain moderate content of arsenic. The gold leaching rate is very low if the ore is treated by the single cyaniding process. If the flotation process is applied to treat the ore, gold recovery rate in the gold concentrate will be high, but the gold concentrate will be hard to sell due to its high content of arsenic.

Given the above characteristics, it is recognized that the following three steps of work shall be conducted to solve this problem.

Firstly, pretreatment of ore should be conducted before cyaniding for extracting gold. This is to reveal the gold from the main gold-bearing sulfide minerals through decomposition of gold carriers by oxidation. At the same time, some harmful elements that would disturb the gold extraction in cyaniding method should be removed out.

Secondly, some chemical substances or reagents should be added in order to control or get rid of the disturbance of some harmful elements to the cyaniding gold extraction.

Thirdly, new, efficient or non-toxic gold leaching solvent should be searched and developed to replace the cyanide in order to solve the environmental pollution thoroughly.

All of the above three measures should be the main orientations of research and development on technologies for hard-processing and hard-smelting ores in the future. However, the pretreatment technique of the gold ores, which are hard to be processed at present, will be the main objective of development and application in the near future, in terms of the technological development trends both at home and abroad.

From the orientation of research and effects of application on the technology for hard-processing and hard-smelting ores abroad, it can be seen that its key issue is to remove the "gold-robbing" property of carbonaceous matters through pre-oxidation or pre-separation. Therefore, the technology for hard-processing and hard-smelting ores mainly refers to the pretreatment technology. At present, the pretreatment technologies that have been developed and applied or are under research include calcination process, pressure oxidation process, bacterial oxidation process, chemical oxidation process, chlorination process and sulfur-bearing reagent oxidation process, etc. Based on the analysis of development trend of pretreatment process and its application extent abroad, it can be seen that the calcination oxidation, pressure oxidation and bacterial oxidation will be the three basic pretreatment processes in the future for treating gold ores which are hard to be processed at present.

In order to better utilize a large quantity of low-grade complicated polymetallic ores in China, it is necessary to develop new processing and smelting agents and separating media, to improve the size and automation level of processing and smelting equipments, based on the actual characteristics of the minerals, then to improve the efficiencies of processing, smelting and leaching processes and the level of ecological environment control.

Special attention should be paid to researches on the technologies for enlarging the processing and smelting equipments and for amplifying process simulation, the vacuum metallurgy, microwave metallurgy and gas metallurgy technologies, the fluidized calcining and extreme media processes, the pressure oxidation, and the combined biological, physical and chemical restoration technologies. With the new separation equipment and environment-friendly processing and smelting agent technology, the critical technologies of thermometallurgy, hydrometallurgy and biology metallurgy should be integrated. Researches on the biological and chemical catalytic process and the method and equipment for large-scale process should be carried out by using the mechanism of interaction among water, minerals and microbes in the nature. The energy-saving and environment-friendly process for comprehensive utilization of mineral resources should be proposed. New biological catalysis and conversion process technologies should be developed. The cycling utilization of reaction media should be strengthened. The purpose of the above measures is to finally achieve a result of zero discharge of waste gas, waste water and waste residue.

Special efforts should be put to develop the combined technologies of pyrometallurgy, thermometallurgy, hydrometallurgy, biology metallurgy and extreme conditions media technology for coordinately process the mineral resources which are hard to be processed and smelted at present, to develop energetically the vacuum metallurgy, gas metallurgy, microwave metallurgy and other efficient metallurgy technologies, to conduct mass flow analysis on mineral circulation metabolism and the optimization design of green industry chain, to develop critical technology of low energy consumption for the energy step-flow, and to design a short-procedure for processing ores from mines to new materials.

With the above researches, a series of core technologies, large equipments and clean production mode, with the independent intellectual property rights, for comprehensive utilization of mineral resources should be established and developed in terms of the catalytic reaction, equipment, procedure and process. Especially, breakthroughs on following technical difficulties should be made.

1) Key technology for directly leaching low-grade nickel copper sulfide ores with high magnesium content.

2) Critical technology and equipment for clean extracting vanadium from vanadium titaniferous magnetite.

3) Technologies for efficient utilizing rare earths, iron and niobium from associated ores.

4) Technology for efficient utilization of mineral resources in salt lakes and oceans.

5) Critical integrated technology for processing and smelting the arsenic and antimony rich silver, copper, lead, zinc polymetallic ores.

6) Technologies for recycling and utilizing iron and manganese from the associated polymetallic ores.

7) Technologies for recycling and utilization of copper, tin and other polymetal associated deposits.

8) Technology for efficient utilization of complicated rare and precious metal deposits.

9) Technology for efficient utilization of useful elements Ni, Mo and PGE in black shales.

10) Critical technology for clean extracting and utilizing gold from ores presently hard to be processed.

11) Technologies for recycling and utilization of paragenic and associated molybdenum deposits that are presently hard to be dressed.

12) Critical technology for comprehensive recycling of valuable elements from copper, lead and zinc tailings.

13) Phosphogypsum comprehensive utilization technology.

14) Sulfuric acid cinder and hard-dressing hematite fluidized calcining technology.

15) Technology for recycling and comprehensive utilization of useful elements from metallurgical scraps.

16) Technology for biological, physical and chemical restoration of the heavy metals polluted soils in the mine areas, the critical technology for plant restoration and crop safety treatment, disposal and reutilization, and the integrated technology for restoration of heavy metal polluted soils.

17) Technology for deactivation of heavily contaminated soils in the mining areas, for reduction of the migration ability and biological effectiveness of harmful elements.

18) Technology for immobilized degradation of organism by microbe in mine areas, the biological surfactant intensified rehabilitation technology, in-situ microorganism repair technology, plant-microbial joint repair technology.

19) Radionuclide contaminated soil control and restoration technology.

20) Technology and process for ecological recovery and reconstitution of mines.

2.5 Resources Substitution and Cyclic Utilization

2.5.1 Status-quo and Development Trend

As it is known to all that mineral resources are non-renewable, and the conventional resources will finally be consumed away. Meanwhile, the rise of newly emerging industries calls for the demand of new raw mineral resources, such as the nano industry requires natural nano raw minerals and the environmental industry requires raw mineral materials for environmental protection. This demand becomes increasingly pressing with the restructure of industry and economy. Therefore, it is imperative to explore new alternative resources incessantly for keeping abreast of the demand at the time. It is believed that to actively study and to develop new alternative resources technology and to explore new alternative resources are the way out to meet the ever-increasing demands for mineral resources in our society, as to develop new energy technology advocated by governments of many countries. In fact, the history of the development of human society is the one that mankind explores new resources incessantly[89].

Currently, various kinds of new alternative resources technologies are shown in China, with good prospective for large-scale industrialization in the future. They may have far-reaching influences on the resources guarantee and the sustainable social and economic development of China in the future. For example, they include the large-scale production technology of basalt (silicates) fiber, the technology for recovering alumina from high aluminum-bearing clay or coal ash, the technology for transforming and utilizing non-water-soluble potash ore, the technology for producing magnesium metal from dolomite, the technology for highly exploiting natural nano and micron minerals (function materials), the technology for using coal ash to control desertification and to afforest, and the technology for recycling and utilizing major metal materials, etc.

From the sequence of elemental abundance in the crust in Fig. 2.11, it can be seen that elements, which have an abundance of over 2% and can be used by mankind as solid raw materials, including silicon, aluminum, iron, calcium, sodium, potassium and magnesium. An overwhelming majority of these elements are existed in forms of silicates. Therefore, it is most promising to choose to develop (aluminum) silicate materials.

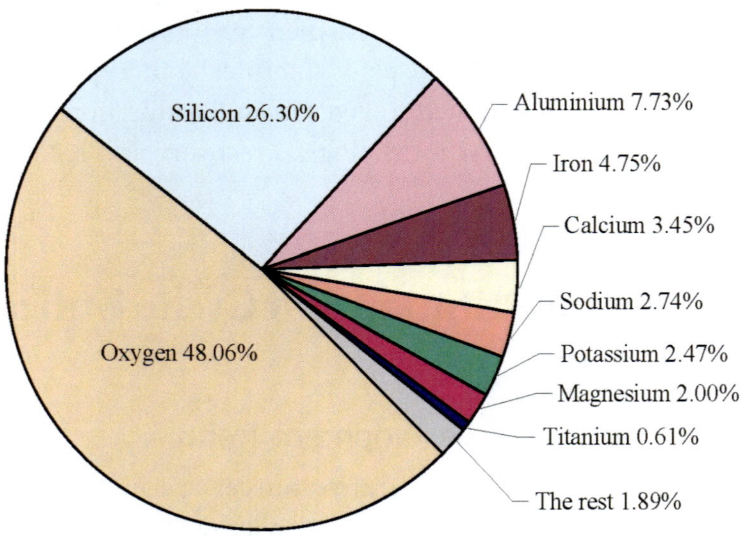

Fig. 2.11 The abundance of elements in the crust

These are various silicate rock fibers, silicate ceramics and various non-metal mineral materials. Among the above elements, only iron, aluminum and magnesium are suitable for making pure metal or alloy materials (calcium, sodium and potassium are too active to be alloy). As iron and aluminum have been highly processed, therefore, to develop magnesium metal is the most promising choice in the field of metal raw materials.

The new resources technologies that have shown preliminary promising prospective can be generally divided into four categories based on their functions.

(1) Alternative Resources for Important Metal Ores

The technology for making alternative resources to replace important metal ores includes the large-scale production technology of basalt (silicate) fiber, the technology for recovering alumina from high aluminum-bearing clay or coal ash, the technology for making magnesium metal from dolomite, the new ceramics technology, etc.

The block metal resources in China such as iron ores, bauxite and copper ores are in critical shortage, and China is highly dependent on imports. Therefore, it is urgent for us to find out their alternative resources. There are three kinds of substitutions by alternative resources. ① The aluminum alloy, steel and other metal materials could be substituted by the composite materials or new type of ceramics, which were reinforced by silicate glass fibers (including basalt fiber); ② High aluminum-bearing kaolinite, coal ash and other non-metal resources could be used as the raw materials for extracting alumina and producing aluminum alloy, in order to supplement the shortage of bauxite resources; ③ Dolomite could be used as the raw materials for the large-scale production of magnesium metal and alloy, in order to supple the shortages of steel and aluminum products.

The continuous basalt fiber is reputed as "green industrial raw material in the 21st century", because basalt is a low-price, pollution-free and non-toxic resource, and it cannot be depleted. The continuous basalt fiber can be used to produce many top-grade composite materials, which could be widely utilized to replace block metal materials such as iron and steel, and aluminum alloy[90] (Fig. 2.12). Currently, the critical technological difficulty is to develop the large-scale production technology of continuous basalt fiber, including large-scale furnace and platinum-alternative large-scale drawbench nozzle plate.

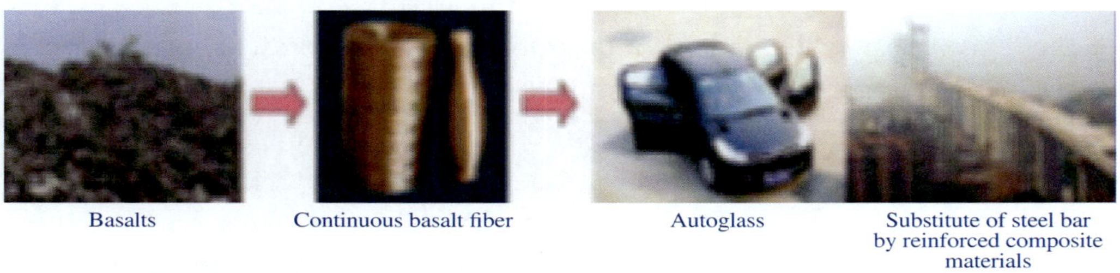

Fig. 2.12 A flow chart showing to produce fiber from basalts, and then to produce autoglass for automobile and reinforced composite materials for construction

High aluminum-bearing coal ash, coal gangue and clays contain a lot of alumina (Al_2O_3). Their alumina resources are far larger than those of the bauxite currently under exploitation. However, they are low in Al_2O_3 grade, high in silicon content and therefore hard to be utilized with conventional technologies at present. In 2007, the amount of discharged coal ash in China was 200 million tons, and this figure is increasing every year. 25% of the discharged coal ash contains over 36% of Al_2O_3. If 80% of them could be recycled, about 14.4 million tons of Al_2O_3 could be obtained, accounting for 72% of the total Al_2O_3 consumption in China (nearly 20 million tons of Al_2O_3) in 2007.

New ceramics have a series of superior physical, chemical and biological properties, and can replace metal materials for producing engine components, which will result in the increase of the life cycle and the maximum speed for the engine and the reduction of its fuel consumption. In addition, new ceramics have been applied into various industrial branches including high temperature, erosion, insulation and vacuum with good results. The key technical difficulties include to reduce the brittleness of ceramics and to improve its pliability and machinability. This requires developing the low specific surface area and high sintering technology of the activated oxide power, and ceramics-group fibrous composite materials, etc.[91-92].

Actually, with the advancement of science and technology and the improvement of people's living standards, demands on new materials by all industries are increased gradually. This requires continuously providing relevant new mineral resources by the mineral industries. For example, in order to achieve light-weight and energy conservation, industries such as the car industry have taken the lead in replacing the steel with the aluminum alloy, and now replacing the aluminum alloy with the high-performance composite materials and magnesium alloy. Magnesium ranks No.8 among all elements in the crust in terms of abundance. Magnesium and its alloy are characterized with light weight and environment-friendly. They are widely applied in the auto and space industries, hence are named as "green engineering material in the 21st century"[93].

(2) Alternative Resources for Important Non-metal Ores

The technology for making alternative resources to replace important non-metal ores mainly includes the technology for transforming and utilizing non-water-soluble potash ore and the technology for recovering and utilizing sulfur in the high sulfur-bearing coal.

The water soluble potash ores in China are in great shortage. Over 90% of them each year is dependent upon imports. Even at present, over the 70% is imported. Therefore, the farmland in China is generally lack of potassium. This has greatly impeded the further increase of the agricultural production. However, China is abundant in potassium-rich silicate rock that is non-water-soluble potassium resource. Statistics shows that the available reserves of soluble potassium in China are only 216 million tons of K_2O. However, preliminary statistics show that the K_2O resources converted from the non-soluble potassium resources are over 5 billion tons, and the prospective resources exceed 10 billion tons. How to develop the potassium-rich silicate for replacing water-soluble potassium has been pursued by Chinese scientists and technicians. It is grateful that a great progress has been made for the utilization of non-water-soluble potassium resources in recent years. For example, K-feldspar and muscovite can be hydrothermally decomposed to nano and sub-micron sized new mineral phases by using alkaline-earth-based stimulation. This could make the wish to be practical (Fig. 2.13).

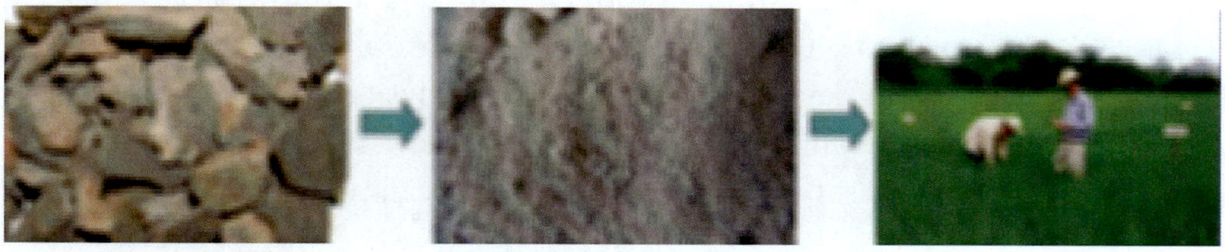

Fig. 2.13 A flow chart showing to produce K-bearing mineral fertilizer by using potassium-rich silicates instead of soluble sylvite and its application

The sulfuric acid is a basic raw material in the chemical industry. Currently, China needs to import a large amount of sulfur to produce sulfuric acid. However, there is a large quantity of high sulfur-bearing coal, which cannot be utilized at present because of its environmental issues. According to the incomplete statistics, the proved reserves of high sulfur-bearing coal in China are 62 billion tons. If the average sulfur content of the high sulfur-bearing coal is taken as 3.2%, the sulfur resources in the coal in China can reach 2 billion tons, which is more than the total proved reserves of sulfur in China (The proved reserves of sulfur in pyrite ores, associated sulfur and brimstone are less than 1.7 billion tons totally). Currently, with the application of the coal water slurry pressure gasification technology, the sulfur recovery rate from the high sulfur-bearing coal can reach over 90%. The largest "coal-made methanol" device in the country, with an annual production capacity of 500 thousand tons, uses high sulfur-bearing coal. The coal water slurry pressure gasification technology has been applied in the high sulfur-bearing coal to methanol transformation project by the Yanzhou Coal Mining Group has made the sulfur recovery of sulfur from the high sulfur-bearing coal reach 91.6%.

(3) New Resources for Newly Emerging Industries

It mainly includes the highly exploitation technology of natural nano-micron minerals (function materials), environmental material technology of clay minerals, nano ceramics technology, gradient ceramics technology, etc.

Nano technology, information technology and biological technology have been reputed as the three mainstream technologies in the new century. Americans even believe that nano technology will become the engine for the economic development in the 21st century. However, the technology for making artificial nanophase materials is complicated, its productive capacity is low, and the cost is high. All these have severely hindered the development of nano industry. In fact, many natural non-metal minerals are in sizes of nanometer and micrometer. They have different crystal morphological characteristics and special properties of physics and material science. They have the advantages and characteristics of general nano particles. They are good raw materials for developing nano materials.

Natural non-metallic nano minerals are pervasive in the nature. They are in large quantities (the reserves are over hundreds of millions of tons) and are inexhaustible, with simple producing process and low producing cost (Fig. 2.14). For example, ① A large amount of natural nano clay minerals in southern China such as kaolinite, paligorskite, halloysite and bentonite; ② The ooze at the modern ocean floor and Maar Lake floor; ③ Kieselguhr; ④ Many nanometer sized meshes in multihole zeolite; ⑤ Ocean polymetal nodules[89].

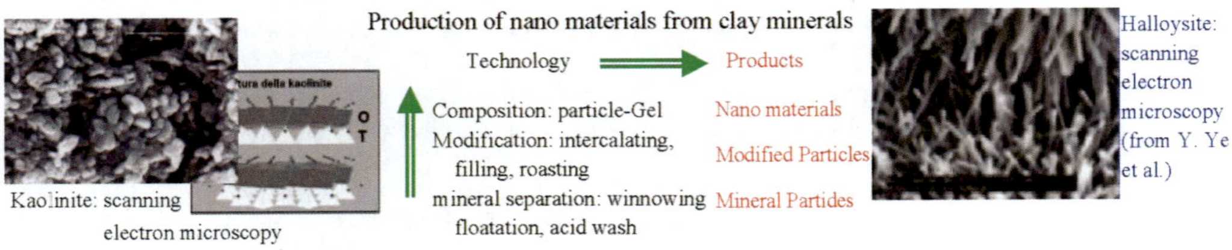

Fig. 2.14 A chart showing nano composite materials produced from clay minerals such as kaolinite and halloysite

In addition, in order to meet the demands for heat preservation and energy conservation building materials, such non-metal minerals as expanded perlite, zeolite and expanded vermiculite are widely used. Earthquake disaster relief calls for light building materials. It is expected that expanded perlite, zeolite, expanded vermiculite and mineral wool would be explored for their application in new areas.

(4) Cyclic Utilization Technology and Waste Reutilization Technology as Advocated in the Recycling Economy Promotion Law of the People's Republic of China

1) Cyclic utilization technology of important metal materials

It mainly includes copper, zinc, iron and steel, and aluminum recycling and reutilization technology.

Though mineral resources are non-renewable, they can be recycled and reused, especially the metals. All metals, ferrous and non-ferrous, can be recycled to become secondary metals. The energy consumption per unit output for producing secondary metal is far lower than that of the primary metal. In addition, the secondary metal recycling process causes much less pollutions to the environment, and it is much easier to be controlled, comparing to the primary metal producing process. The secondary metal industry will become emerging sunrise industry in China. Therefore, the cyclic utilization of metals is one of the major means to solve the shortage of resources, to which all developed countries have given high attention[94]. At present, 45% of the steel output is from the smelting of steel scraps in the world, 40% of copper is recycled from copper scraps. However, the scrap recycling rate of China is only about 1/3–1/2 of the world average. In China's steel output, only 15–20% is recycled from steel scraps. With the development of China's economy, the steel scraps produced will be largely increased. To strengthen recycling of iron and steel scraps is of special significance for the reduction of costs, improvement of economic benefits and protection of environment. It is also one of the major means to solve the contradictions between supply and demand of iron ores.

According to the statistics of international copper research organization, the secondary recovered and extracted copper in European countries accounts for 41% of the total copper consumed. Currently, China annually imports over 10 million tons of steel scraps, 3 million tons of copper-bearing wastes and 2.5 million tons of other non-ferrous-bearing waste. Nevertheless, the recycling and reutilization level of non-ferrous metals of China is much lower than that of the world's average (Table 2.2). It is urgently required to develop advanced relevant technologies and to issue relevant supporting policies.

2) Recycling technology of industrial wastes

The recycling technology of industrial wastes includes the technology for production of cementitious material from industrial waste, the building material fabrication technology, the coal gangue fertilization technology, and the desertification controlling and afforestation technology by using coal ash, etc.

Table 2.2 A comparison between recycling rate of non-ferrous metals of China and that of the world average [95]

Country	Item	Capacity in 2003 (thousand tons)	Proportion of output of secondary resources to that of primary resources in 2003 (%)	Average annual rate from 1992 to 2003 (%)
China	Secondary copper	288.4	16.27	28.39
	Secondary aluminum	114.8	20.6	4.85
	Secondary lead	247.7	15.70	15.76
World	Secondary copper	5,518	36.24	37.81
	Secondary aluminum	7,659	21.48	24.21
	Secondary lead	3,087	44.98	45.09

Most of the conventional resources are characterized with high pollution, high discharge and high energy consumption. With the advancement of human civilization, a large amount of various kinds of industrial wastes and pollutants are discharged and stockpiled. The largest solid wastes are coal ash, coal gangue of coal mines and tailings of metal mines. The annually discharged coal ash in China reaches 200 million tons. In principle, these solid wastes can be regarded as the non-metal mineral resources for reutilization[96]. The key is that the appropriate application technology and favorable policy support are need. Therefore, to develop waste reutilization technology in order to change wastes into valuables, to establish recycling economy, and to build ecological civilization are the main components of new resources technology.

For example, the condensate stone, a new building material, is made with a certain ratio of silicate waste residue (coal ash and slag, etc.) (90–99%) and some diagenetic agent (1–10%) designed on the basis of mechanism of geological diagenesis. It is a kind of water-insolvable cemented material formed through a certain procedure of milling process. The condensate stone can replace cement/concrete in many cases, with much better function[92]. As it is known to all, the production of cement, which is widely used material in the building industry, is characterized with high energy consumption and high waste discharge per unit output. The producing process of the condensate stone needs only "one milling" rather than "one calcination and two milling" as required by the production of cements. This clean production technology saves energy and resources, and reduces discharged waste. Meanwhile, it makes the reutilization of a large quantity of silicate waste possible. This is a typical case of recycling economy.

In fact, innovations of resources substitution and cyclic utilization technology will not only solve the shortage of resources effectively, but also drive the development of many emerging industries, then further promote new economic growth points, create new opportunities for the development of economy in China and play an important role in improving China's industrial structure. Therefore, it is imperative to plan for developing the resources substitution and cyclic utilization technology and to build new resources economic system in view of driving the development of emerging industries, improving industrial structure, transforming the economic development (growth) mode, changing resources consumption mode and building an innovation-oriented society. Fig. 2.15 is a roadmap for the development of this area.

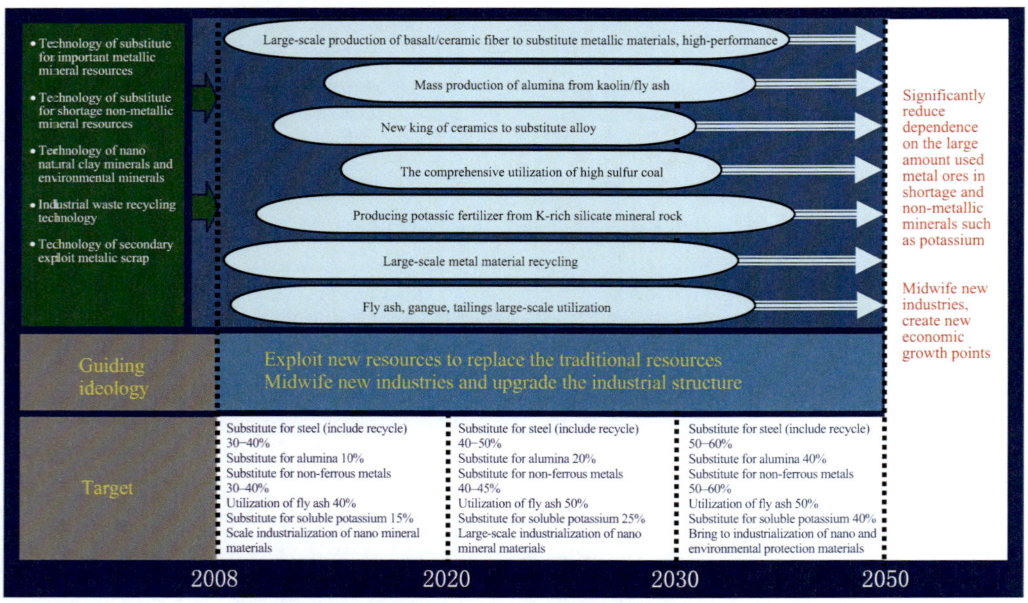

Fig. 2.15 Technological development roadmap for alternative and recycling minerals

2.5.2 Overall Objectives and Objectives at Different Stages to 2050

(1) Overall Objectives to 2050

The overall objectives from present to 2050 for developing resources substitution and cyclic utilization technology include following aspects. ① To substitute some urgently needed metal and non-metal resources for relieving the shortage of resources in China. ② To provide new resources and new raw materials support for the socioeconomic development of China, particularly to provide new high performance raw materials for the new emerging industries. ③ To reutilize wastes, to change wastes into valuables, to build recycling economy and to build new ecological civilization. The overall objectives from present to 2050 are to greatly reduce China's dependence on urgently needed metal minerals (about 40–60%) and non-metal minerals such as potash ores (about 40%), to promote the development of emerging industries group and to create new economic growth points through innovations and large-scale industrialization of the important metal minerals substitution technology, the urgently needed non-metal minerals substitution technology, the nano material and environmental-friendly material technologies by transforming natural clay minerals, the industrial waste reutilization technology, and the metal scrap and waste recycling technology.

(2) Objectives at Different Stages

1) In terms of substitution of metal and non-metal raw materials

① The silicate fiber and its composite materials will be used to substitute steel. The substitute rate will be expected to reach 5–10% in 2020, 10–15% in 2030, and 15–20% in 2050, respectively.

② High alumina-bearing coal ash or high alumina-bearing clays such as kaolinite will be used to substitute bauxite as the raw materials for recycling alumina. The substitute rate will be expected to achieve 10% (about 3 million tons of alumina) in 2020, 20% in 2030 and 40% in 2050, respectively.

③ The non-water-soluble potassium in the potassium-rich silicates will be converted into water-soluble potassium to replace water-soluble potash ores for producing potash fertilizer. The substitute rate will be expected to reach 15% of the potash fertilizer for agricultural usage in 2020, 25% in 2030 and 40% in 2050, respectively.

④ The sulfur in high sulfur-bearing coal will be recycled for relieving the shortage of sulfur. The sulfur substitute rate will be expected to reach 15% in 2020, 20% in 2030, and 30% in 2050.

2) In terms of providing new raw materials for emerging industries

① Dolomite will be used to produce high-performance and light magnesium alloy. Its annual output will be expected to reach 5 million tons in 2020, 7 million tons in 2030 and 9 million tons in 2050, respectively.

② Natural nano mineral materials will be provided for nano industry. Their annual output will be expected to reach 1 million tons in 2020, 2 million tons in 2030 and 4 million tons in 2050, respectively.

③ The high-performance silicate fiber composite materials will be put into wide application in such areas as aviation, automobile, shipbuilding, wind power generation, conduits, high-speed railway, large bridges and building construction.

3) In terms of waste recycling and reutilization

① The scrap and waste iron and steel will be recycled and reutilized. The rate between the annually recycled steel and the total consumed steel products will be expected to reach 25–30% in 2020, 30–35% in 2030 and 35–40% in 2050, respectively. The cyclic utilization rate of non-ferrous metals will be expected to reach 30–40% in 2020, 40–45% in 2030 (the mean level of development countries at present) and 50–60% in 2050, respectively.

② The new building materials made from industrial waste such as condensate stones will partly substitute cement, with expected substitute rate of 15% in 2020, 25% in 2030 and 35% in 2050, respectively.

③ Breakthroughs on the technology for controlling desertification and afforestation by using coal ash should be made. The technology should be widely applied. The treated areas by this technology should reach tens of thousands of square kilometers by 2020, and hundreds of thousands of square kilometers by 2030, respectively.

④ The overall utilization rate of coal ash will be expected to reach 40% in 2020, 50% in 2030, and 70% in 2050, respectively. The utilization rate of tailings of metal mines will be expected to reach 30% in 2020, 50% in 2030, and 70% in 2050, respectively.

2.5.3 Major Scientific Issues to be Solved to Attain the Objectives

(1) Scientific and Technological Issues Concerning Major Metal Minerals Substitution Resources

1) Large-scale production of silicate fiber

Major scientific and technological issues related to the large-scale production of silicate fiber include the thermodynamic characteristics and dynamics mechanism of high temperature fusion and rapid condensation of different silicate rocks, the relationship between silicate melt viscosity and temperature variation path and velocity, the surficial features (such as wetting angle changes) and dynamics process of the high temperature silicate melt when it is in contact with different refractory materials, the optimized temperature bracket for the filber formation from silicate melt and its controlling technology, the relationship between silicate composition and the fiber properties, the relationship between fiber property and surface sizing, the homogenization mechanism of high temperature melts and the large-size proplatinum drawbench nozzle plate technology.

2) Recovering alumina from high alumina-bearing coal ash, coal gangue and clays

Major issues include the conditions and mechanism for hydrothermal decomposition of Al_2O_3 from coal ash, coal gangue and clays, the chemical behaviors and separation mechanism of alumina, silicon oxide, calcium oxide and iron oxide in alkaline solution and acidic solution.

3) Technology for the development of magnesium metal and alloy from dolomite resources

Major issues include the high temperature reduction thermometric characteristics and dynamic mechanism of magnesium oxide, the high temperature sublimation behavior and mechanism of pure magnesium metal, the microstructure of alloy formed with magnesium and aluminum and other metals and its constraint to the alloy property.

(2) Scientific and Technological Issues Concerning Substitution for Urgently Needed Non-metal Minerals

1) Conversion and utilization of non-water-soluble potassium-rich silicates

Major issues include the mechanism of K-feldspar/mica hydrothermal decomposition and the new mineral formation in moderately hot water under the effect of alkali-earth-stimulation, the formation and preservation mechanism of nano to submicron mineral crystalline phases, and the absorption mechanism of plant root to nano-submicron minerals.

2) Recovery of sulfur from the high sulfur-bearing coal

It requires the technology for efficiently recovering surlfur from the high sulfur-bearing coal, especially the thermometric and dynamics of the coal water slurry pressure gasification.

(3) New Resources Technology for Relevant Emerging Industries

It includes the surficial interface behavior and remodeled activation mechanism of natural nano and micron clay minerals, and the micro-structure characterization techniques.

(4) Scientific and Technological Issues Concerning Industrial Waste Recycling and Reutilization

1) The desertification controlling and afforestation technology by using coal ash.

2) Building material fabrication technology by using tailings

3) The rapid hydration and hardening mechanism of industrial residue by using diagenetic agents.

4) The coal gangue fertilization technology.

5) The cyclic utilization technology of scrap and waste metals.

2.5.4 Major Technical Means to Attain the Objectives

(1) Silicate (including Basalt) Fiber Large-scale Production Technology

The current continuous basalt fiber production technology can only be applied to small-scale production. Therefore, the total global output hasn't exceeded 10 thousand tons yet for many years. In addition, the production costs are relatively high, which makes the wide application difficult. It is imperative now to organize multi-disciplinary technological endeavors to make breakthroughs on the large-scale production technology. Firstly, according to the design and implementation experience of glass fiber tank furnace and the basalt fiber proplatimum crucible, the design of the tank furnace for basalt fiber should be conducted. Secondly, the optimum design to fuel gas supply system and firing system, ore material addition system, fume discharging system, high temperature melt homogenization system, controlling system of melt liquid level, and melt diversion and distribution system, that are all required for tank furnace, should be conducted. Thirdly, the optimal proposal should be worked out based on the nozzle plate structural design and the existed drawbench system, nozzle plate power supply system, surface sizing circulatory system and water cooling circulatory system. With the help of theoretical analysis and engineering computation, the proposal should be reviewed and revised back and force. Finally, the complete technical proposal and drawings should be worked out, and then the engineering practice and experiment should be carried out. It includes the following technical difficulties.

1) Large proplatinum drawbench nozzle plate

According to the properties of silicate melt, the proper high temperature refractory materials (such as cermet) should be selected to replace the costly rhodium-platinum alloy for designing and producing 800–4,000 holes large-scale drawbench nozzle plate. The proplatinum materials must have properties including high temperature resistance, high-temperature erosion resistance (especially resisting high-temperature erosion of basalt magma), high temperature oxidation resistance, high mechanical strength at high temperature, good anti-deformation capacity at high temperature, good thermo-electrical performance, easy to be machined and appropriate basalt melt surface wetting angle. According to characteristics of high viscosity and narrow drawbench shaping temperature range of basalt melt, it is necessary to study and develop the constant current and thermostatically controlled nozzle plate electrification heating controller in order to further improve the controlling precision of thermo-regulation of the nozzle plate. Meanwhile, the structure of nozzle plate should be reasonably designed in order to improve the temperature homogeneity in the drawbench area of the nozzle plate in order to ensure the stable operation of drawbench.

2) Pneumoelectric multistage heating system design and high-temperature melt homogenization technique study

Various technical measures should be adopted to ensure the melt on the nozzle plate reaches consistency and stability in terms of composition and temperature. It includes reasonable pneumoelectric multistage heating system design, furnace combustion and temperature controlling system design and high-temperature agitation design, etc. According to the requirement of sufficient ore fusion, homogenization, and distributing flow to different nozzle plates, distribution of burner nozzle and electrical heating bodies should be designed properly, and various power supply should be selected rationally for electrical heating bodies, in order to make the temperature field in the furnace maximally meet the requirements of sufficient ore melting, homogenization and distributing diversion.

3) Research on parameters of tank furnace drawbench forming process for large-scale nozzle plate

There are large differences among angles and tension deviations of fibers drawn from nozzles at different locations on the nozzle plate. Therefore, they are likely to result in fiber breakage. In order to ensure the stable operation of drawbench, we must adjust the operation height according to the structure of the nozzle plate and adjust the relative position of lubricator and beam concentration wheel to ensure the uniformity of fiber tension. In addition, we need to work out the appropriate drawbench velocity, processing temperature and height of melt liquid surface for 400–1,000 holes nozzle plates.

4) Surface soaker and soaking technology appropriate for the product

(2) Technology for Recovering Alumina from High Alumina-bearing Coal Ash and High Alumina-bearing Clays

It include the high temperature high pressure (HTHP) reactor technology for the hydrothermal decomposition of alumina (250°C, saturated vapor pressure), and the technologies and equipments for separating alumina, silicon oxide, calcium oxide and iron oxide in alkaline solution and acidic solution.

(3) Technology for Recovering Magnesium Metal from Dolomite

There is a large amount of dolomite resources in China. The conventional "pidgeon process" we currently used is a process that dolomite, as the raw material, was burned in the reduction pot with silicon-iron alloy as the reducer. Though this process only needs small investment, it cannot be used for continuous production due to its low productive capacity and unsuitable for large-scale production. It will result in severe environmental pollution. It is characterized with high labor intensity, high energy consumption per unit output and high production costs. Various ways are proposed for technically improving the process.

1) The substitution of iron-silicon alloy by silicon-aluminum alloy as the reducer will result in 1–1.5 times increase of the output and the reduction of energy consumption and pollutant discharge per unit output.

2) The substitution of fuel coal by fuel gas for the process will greatly reduce the discharge of CO_2.

3) The substitution of the intermittent production procedure with continuous production procedure will greatly improve the productive capacity. Currently, the semi-continuous production mode is in application.

4) The improvement of the heat conduction of the reduction pot by adopting the radiation heat transferring mode will greatly increase the productive capacity.

5) The improvement of the following indices, such as the reduction cycle is less than or equal to 8 hours and the material-magnesium ratio is smaller than or equal to 5, will result in the life cycle of the reduction pot that is more than or equal to 8 months.

(4) Technology for Hydrothermal Interrelation Fertilization of Potassium and Other Elements in Potassium-rich Silicate Rocks

Based on the existing technologies, it is necessary to carry out organized researches on the technology for fertilizing potassium-rich silicates on the purpose of reducing the cost, improving the rate of conversion, and increasing the productive capacity. Main issues are listed below.

1) The high-active calcium oxide calcinations technology.

2) The research and development of efficient activator for hydrothermal reaction.

3) To improve the operating temperature and pressure of the reactor to 250°C and the saturated vapor pressure, respectively.

4) To test the optimal formulation system and the optimal temperature and pressure conditions.

(5) Nano-technology for Natural Clay Minerals

Technical pathway is from processing and purifying, to property modification to recombination.

1) It is necessary to process and purify natural clay minerals which are normally in forms of multi-mineral phases. The ore processing technologies including the ordinary particle gravity (including centrifugal force field) sorting and flotation technology, ultrafine particles sorting technology and high molecule flocculation sorting technology should be mainly applied. The purification technology should be applied are still the acid and alkali treatment and burning and calcinations treatment of clay ores.

2) The purpose of property modification of clay is to make the micron crystal particles of clay minerals with special property and function. The modification technology includes activation (acid activation, alkaline activation, three-dimensional space activation, etc.), intercalation, post support, exposure, filling, dispersing, etc.

3) Recombination is a step to form nano product. It includes the recombination of modified micron particles and recombination of various gelling agents.

(6) High-performance Condensate-stone Technology

This technology includes to develop various kinds of high-performance diagenetic agents for relevant different industrial residues, and to improve the comprehensive material indices of the condensate stone which was formed by rapid hydration and hardening.

2.6 Global Allocation of Mineral Resources

2.6.1 Status-quo and Development Trend

(1) The Optimization of Global Allocation of Mineral Resources is a Main Subject of Economic Globalization

The mineral resources in the Earth are unevenly distributed. Their spatial and temporal distribution regularities are resulted from the long-term evolution of the Earth substances in the geologic history, and are dependent on geologic structural environment and metallogenic setting, without limitation by the current state boundaries or administrative divisions. Therefore, the mineral resources endowments in different countries and regions vary greatly. This unevenness results in the uneven distribution of mineral resources among countries in terms of type and quantity, and the high unevenness among countries in terms of the per capita resources and the number of resource types.

In terms of major mineral resources quantity, the iron ore deposits are mainly distributed in eastern Europe and former Soviet Union, America and Australia, etc, with very little in Middle East and Africa. Copper deposits are mainly concentrated in northern America and southern America of the Pacific belt. Aluminum is mainly concentrated in Guinea, Brazil, Australia, Jamaica and India, in which there are over 73.4% of the total bauxite in the world (Fig. 2.16).

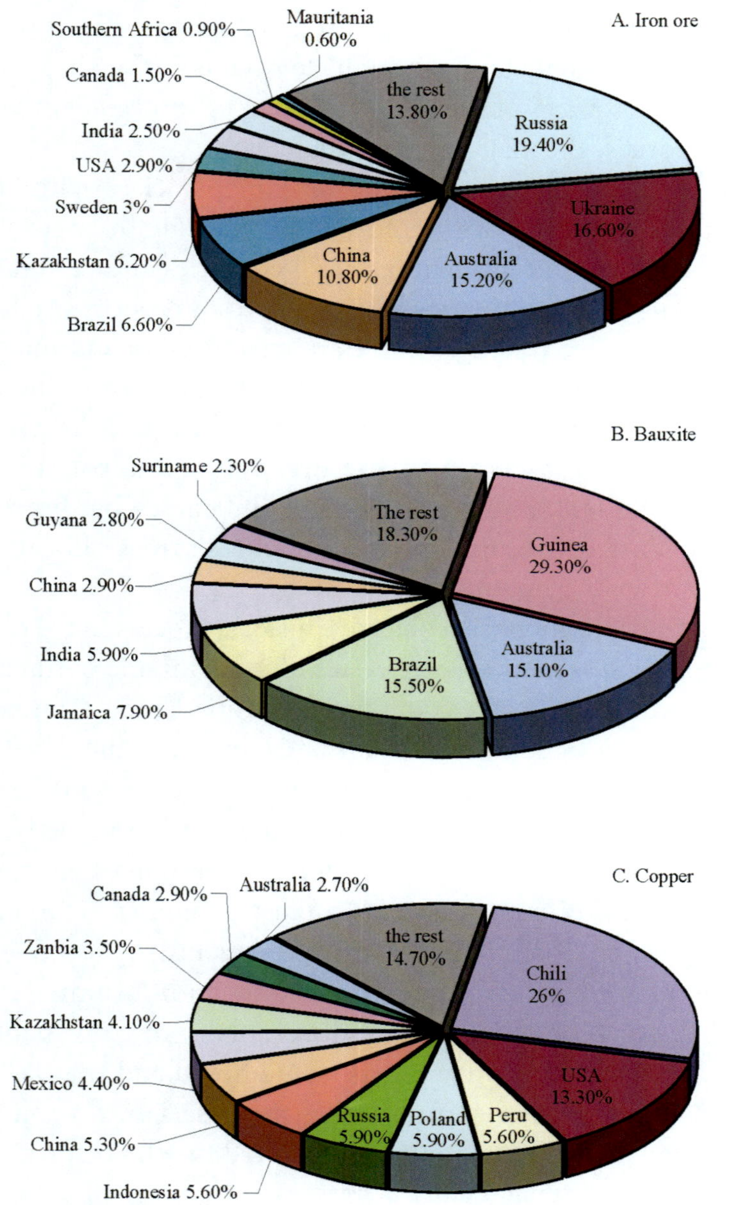

Fig. 2.16 The reserves of iron ores, bauxite and copper in different countries[97]

In terms of countries, southern Africa is known for diamond, gold, platinum and chromite, Chile is known for copper, Russia, Ukraine, Brazil and Australia are known for iron, Canada is known for sylvite, and Guinea is known for bauxite.

The per capita resources of China are low, only about 58% of the world's average. Though China is known for its rare earths, tungsten, tin, antimony and molybdenum, it is lacking of sylvite, copper, iron, aluminum, manganese and other important block minerals.

In fact, no single country can meet its demands for minerals solely dependent on the resources of itself. Countries do need to import more or less some minerals of shortage, and to export some resources of abundant. This gives rise to the complicated situation that all countries and regions in the world are dependent on and constrained by each other on mineral resources. Therefore, when people are discussing the mineral resources supply safety system of their country, they must not only know a complete situation of their own resources, but also know the resources properties and resources strategy of other countries and regions (especially the major mineral suppliers).

In fact, in the development history of human society, natural resources endowment used to be one of the most important factors determining the geographic divisions of social functions of all countries and regions. However, with the economic globalization speed up, this resources-oriented traditional industrial structure is collapsing. People are paying more and more attention to the regional/global resources optimization and allocation in the framework of regional economic integration/economic globalization. When developing countries such as China take over the manufacturing role of developed countries, a huge amount of mineral resources and energy has been demanded in the country. This will transform the global resources allocation pattern against the backdrop of economic globalization.

Economic globalization is an objective historic process in the development of human history and is an inevitable result of pursuing the optimal economic interests by all economies in the commercial and marketing economic system. Modern transportation, communication and especially the development of information network technology have provided objective conditions for this kind of exchanges. The essence of economic globalization is the free flow and optimized allocation of all production factors and resources globally in order to seek the maximized economic benefits. In fact, in modern market economic society, scarcely any economy can develop independently.

It can be seen that the optimal global allocation of mineral resources is a main subject of economic globalization. This is an irreversible trend of development. Human beings live on the same homeland that is our planet. How to optimally utilize the resources on Earth for serving human beings and to build a healthy, harmonious and sustainable homeland for mankind are common questions for human beings at present.

Of course, the concept of the optimal allocation of global resources is totally different from the colonists' looting of resources from small and weak countries in the past. The essence of global allocation of resources we are talking about is the deeper cooperation and common development on the basis of peaceful coexistence, mutual benefits and complementation of advantages, in order to build a harmonious world community of common prosperity. Through the optimal allocation of mineral resources, the maximum value of natural resources would be to exploit for serving human beings.

As pointed out by Premier Jiabao Wen of the PRC, the economic construction in China depends on the global allocation pattern of mineral resources. As a developing country with the largest population and strategic importance, China cannot develop single industrial structure like some small countries. The demands of complete self-contained industrial system for mineral resources are omnifarious. Therefore, the mineral resources strategy of China should be made in a view of the optimized allocation of global resources.

China, as a country abundant in resources but poor in per capita resources must adopt the two resources and two markets strategy featuring with "mutual exchanges of needed resources to ensure resources security through reliance mainly on the own resources of the country itself with partly supplemented from the rest of the world". As pointed out by Premier Jiabao Wen of the PRC, the geologic researches need to be strategically adjusted to focus on not only the dominant minerals in China but also the capacity of resources supplies from neighboring countries.

(2) Relationship Between the Differences of Social Wealth Accumulated and the Consumption of Mineral Resources

The great difference of social wealth among various countries is a major contradiction during present economic globalization, and is also a basic factor causing social instability in the world. The social wealth per capita is a reflection of how wealthy countries with various populations are. In terms of social wealth, the indices closely related to mineral resources can be represented by cars, railways, highways and airports. According to the statistics in 2000, every one hundred Americans have 75 cars, 50–60 times of that of Chinese. The length of highway per capita is 0.47km for the world, whereas it is 23km for the USA, which is 49 times of that for the world, and 23 times of that for China.

The per capita infrastructure and social wealth per unit of area of the developed countries exceed those of the developing countries by several times or even dozens of times (Fig. 2.17). This is extraordinarily discordant with the reserves of their natural resources. This is a record of industrialization process in which the rapid economic development of the developed countries was relied on the high consumption of natural resources, which were mostly or even all from other countries, per capita for a rather long period of time. Japan, a country with small amount of mineral reserves, has banned the mining at home for quite a long time. During and after the Second World War, Japan has studied, ascertained and exploited minerals of other countries in various ways.

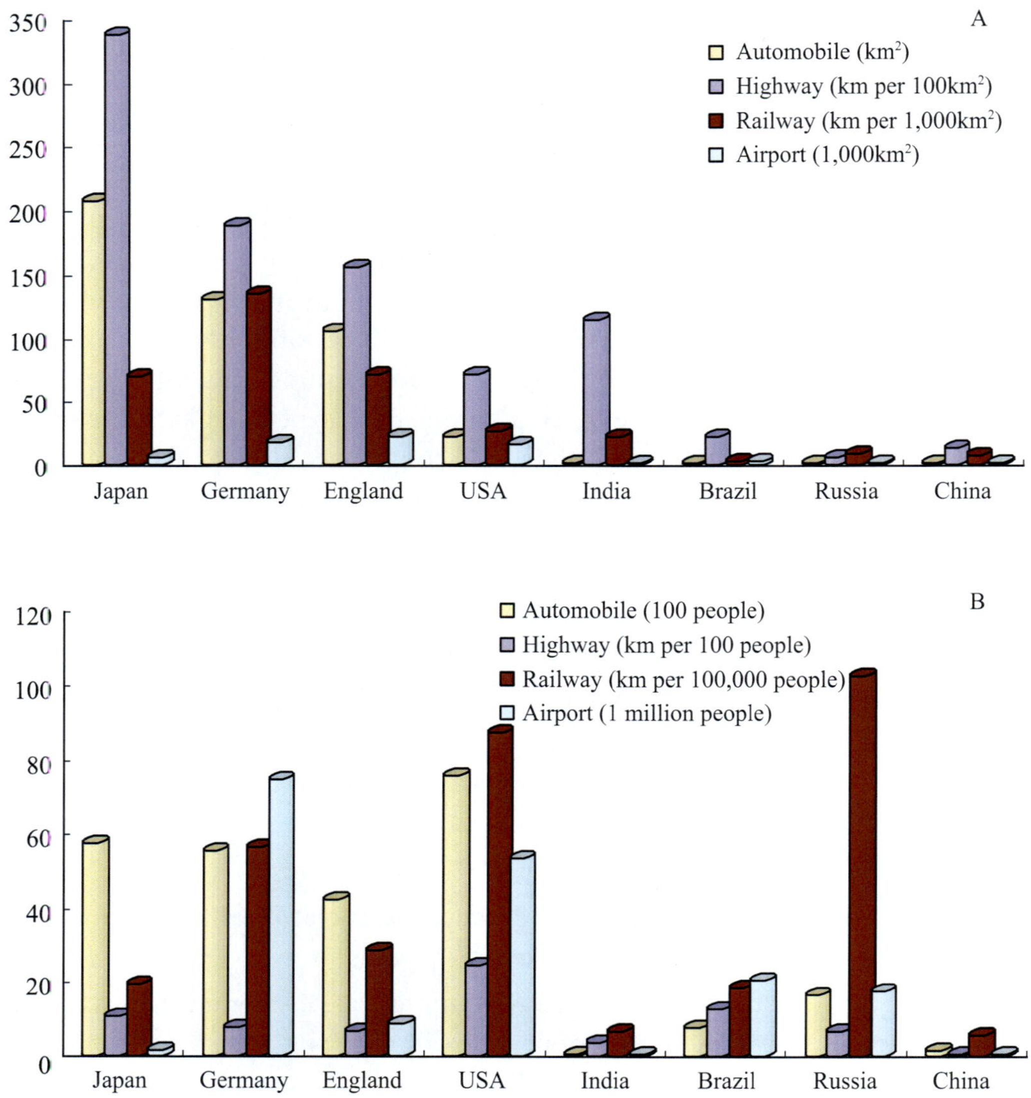

Fig. 2.17 A, the comparison of automible, road, railway and airport in per unit area in some countries; B, the comparison of automible, road, railway and airport for unit population in some countries[97]

As a matter of fact, even when the globalization was not as full-fledged as it is today, the per capita occupied and consumed mineral resources are not calculated based on the actual quantity of resources of their home countries. The industrialization of Britain and USA, which lasts 200 years and 100 years respectively, consumed a large amount of mineral resources[97]. In Britain and other western countries such as Japan, the USA and Germany, the aluminum possession rate per capita is nearly zero. In Britain, Japan and Germany, the iron ore and copper ore reserves are far less than the average level of the world. Most of the minerals they consumed during their industrialization ware supplied by other countries. When their industrialization was completed, their demands for some basic metals were somewhat declined, but were still a large amount. However, the rapid economic development of the developing countries, which are currently in the accelerating process of industrialization, resulted in the gradual increase of demands on mineral resources. Even though, the developed countries, whose population is less than 15% of the total population of the world, still annually consume about 62% of total petroleum consumed annually in the world, 62% of aluminum, and over 50% of coal, steel, and copper metals, respectively. However, the developing countries, whose population is more than 79% of the total population of the world, only annually consume about 31% of total energy consumed annually in the world, 32–45% of aluminum, coal, steel, and copper metals, respectively. It should be pointed out that the rate between the amount of energy and metals consumed by the developed countries and that produced by them in their own countries is extremely unreasonable, as major amount of energy and metal resources they consumed were imported from the developing countries.

The industrialization of the western developed countries was completed in 1970s, whereas many developing countries including China have just entered into the industrialization process on the basis of the rapid economic development in recent ten years. This resulted in the profound changes of the international mineral resources situation. The essence of industrialization process is that the natural resources are transformed into social wealth by human beings. The rapid economic development and social wealth accumulation are obtained on the basis of the consumption and depletion of natural resources. In addition, other two more points should be stressed. ① Natural resources are global, and not evenly distributed according to population and region; ② The process of industrialization of different countries is not the same. Their consumption of and demands for natural resources and hitherto control over global resources are varied greatly. This resulted in that the globalization of mineral resources has never been as important as it is today in international affairs and economic development.

2.6.2 Two Main Subjects in Global Allocation of Mineral Resources for China

There are two subjects in global allocation of mineral resources for China. One is to exchange and complement dominant mineral resources with friendly countries on the basis of mutual benefits. The other is to develop resources in open seas, Polar Regions and some other areas shared by mankind (within the framework of International Laws).

(1) The Exchange and Complementation of Resources with Friendly Countries on the Basis of Mutual Benefits and Optimization of Allocation

In view of national security, important overseas resources bases should not be far away separated from oceans. Preference goes to those neighboring countries. In case of emergencies, we will not be restricted by naval blockade. Therefore, in early 2006, the State Council issued the "Neighboring Countries First Guideline" on strengthening geologic work.

According to our geographical features and abundance of resources in the world, it is proposed that China should adopt in its resources diplomacy as "the guideline giving precedence to neighboring countries in its north, developing actively Africa and giving some attentions to southern America and Oceania".

The neighboring countries in the north of China should be give precedence. Most of them are rich in mineral resources. Along our border, a number of large-scale and super large-scale deposits were found. From Central Asian countries, to Mongolia, to northern China (Xinjiang - Inner Mongolia – three provinces in the Northeastern China) and further to Far East of Russia, there is the palaeo-Asian metallogenic province, one of the three major global metallogenic domains, in which there are lots of world-class metal deposits, with abundant resources that could complement with the shortage of China. These resources are distributed in the less populated and vast areas, in which survey, exploration and exploitation were undertaken at low level, with great potential for future exploitation.

An obvious feature in modern geopolitics is the coordinate unification of the resources center and the geographical center. Neighboring countries in the north of China, which share a border of as long as over 10,000 kilometers, not only have abundant mineral resources but also have common national interests and traditional friendship with China. Most of them are members of Shanghai Cooperation Organization. Our cooperative relationship in business and trade and other areas are becoming closer and closer. These neighboring countries have advantages in terms of geopolitics, transportation, labor cost, and technical adaptability. Thus, It is believed that they are very suitable for establishing mineral resources bases abroad for China. In contrast, the South Asian countries, in which there are abundant resources too, have huge pressure of natural resources on themselves due to their large populations. More likely, they will become our rivals rather than suppliers of mineral resources.

There is an area of about 6.20 million square kilometers, but a population of less than 10 million in the Far East of Russia. There is abundant energy, ferrous metal and non-ferrous metal resources in this area which is reputed as the only existed and unexploited natural resources bank in the world at present. It is indicated that there are 9.6 billion tons of petroleum resources, 14 trillion cubic meters of natural gas, and 18.1 billion tons of proved coal reserves (about 60% of the total in Russia). Furthermore, there are about 29 billion tons of hydrocarbons in the coastal continental shelf of the Far East of Russia.

Mongolia, which has an area of 1.56 million Square kilometers and a population of 2.5 million, has rich metal deposits and coal resources. In early years, Mongolia was entirely relied on USSR for the exploration and exploitation of mineral resources, as it has no its own exploration and mining system. Its exploration of mineral resources is low in degree, and its resources potential is huge. After the collapse of the Soviet Union, the ores prospecting and exploitation rights were mainly controlled by Canadian and Australian companies. For example, in recent years Ivanhoe Mines, a Canadian mining company, discovered a copper-gold deposit near the border between China and Mongolia, with contained copper reserves of nearly 20 million tons in the primarily controlled orebodies.

Kazakstan is a country with an area of 2.717 million Square kilometers. The level of geologic work there is high. It is one of the countries with the most abundant mineral resources in the world. In the country, there are many world-class deposits. The dominant resources in the country include petroleum, natural gas, coal, iron, manganese, chromite, nickel, cobalt, copper, molybdenum, lead, zinc, bauxite, gold and uranium[98]. At present, a large number of base metal and precious metal deposits have been found, and numerous to be discovered and exploited. According to data of the Energy and Mineral Resources Ministry of Kazakstan, Kazakstan ranks No.1 in the world for its barite reserves, No.2 for its chromium and phosphate rock reserves, No. 3 for its copper, lead and zinc reserves, No.4 for its molybdenum reserves, No. 6 for its gold reserves and No. 8 for its iron ore reserves, respectively.

Therefore, it is suggested that the regional economic integration in this area should be promoted within the framework of Shanghai Cooperation Organization (SCO), in order to promote the common rapid economic development. In fact, the regional economic integration based on the geography is the main manifestation of economic globalization, such as EU and NAFTA.

The complement of advantages and moderate disparity in economic development are the precondition for in-depth cooperation. As for members of the SCO, their economic development level is at different levels, economic structures are at different stages, and resources conditions have their own characteristics. Central Asian countries, Mongolia and Far East of Russia are rich in natural resources, but low in populations, shortage of labor force, and lack of funds for development. However, China has sufficient workforce of cheap prices, big markets, rapid and powerful, economic growth, and substantive capital reserves. This complementation has enormous potential for dynamic economic growth. Once the economic free trading process is started among members of the SCO, it will become a paragon among many free trading areas. Members of the SCO will be benefited from the process.

For this reason, it is suggested that we should expedite the regional economic integration in the northern part of China while we are strengthening the cooperation among countries of the SCO. Meanwhile, we should pay attention to interface with neighboring countries in the north of China in terms of market system, industrial configuration, logistics system, information network, allocation of resources, and ecological environment, etc.

1) Market integration includes the integration of product market, capital market, raw material market, technology market, intellectual property market, labor market and talent market. It is necessary to create an open, regularized market environment that is geared to international standards, to improve various market systems and to form various markets community, to create conditions for activating full function of the market mechanism, in order to promote the inter-regional free flow of production factors, especially to realize inter-regional free flow of capital, which is the key to the regional economic integration.

2) Industrial integration is to form rational distribution framework of industrial branches based on regional advantages and to form all-win and mutually beneficial industrial chain through complementation of advantages each other, in order to rationalize regional industrial structure and to improve the overall economic benefits and competitiveness.

3) Integration of transportation infrastructure and power line grid is to carry out integrated planning of express lines such as highway and railway, to expedite the transnational and inter-regional passages and supporting facilities, to improve the transportation, logistics and power grid in order to shorten the distances between China and neighboring countries and to really cut down the costs of regional economic development.

4) Information integration is to smash information blockade and to establish intercommunication and sharing mechanism of information and resources, to jointly conduct market surveys, to establish "Information Cooperation Network", and to establish modern market information platform and comprehensive information platform in order to let enterprises achieve maximized economic benefits through the unblocked information highway.

5) Integration of resources allocation is to entirely optimize resources allocation within the framework of the whole development of the SCO under the precondition of following the market economic rules, to comprehensively plan the overall industrial configuration and distribution on the basis of the combination of the resources-oriented and the market-oriented factors. In terms of geological tectonics, all members of the SCO are in the paleo-Asian metallogenic province, and have similar geological tectonics and same metallogenic features.

6) Integration of ecological environment is to carry out cooperation in the area of ecological environment, to conduct unified planning in the field of the water resources and ecological building as soon as possible among all members of the SCO, in order to achieve mutual-benefits and to build a harmonious homeland. This is because there are very close relationships among all members o the SCO in terms of mountains and rivers, vegetations and deserts, air flow, cloud cluster and sandstorm.

(2) The Development of Resources in Open Seas, Polar Regions and Other Areas Shared by Mankind

1) Mineral resources in Polar Regions

Researches and studies on the Polar Regions conducted by many countries do involve more or less some intentions of territorial occupation and resources possession. The Antarctic expedition in early times involves strong intentions of land grabbing. Though the Antarctic Treaty has banned the occupation of territory in Polar Regions, many countries still have obvious intentions of land occupation and resources possession in their activities. This is because, like other continents, the Antarctica has various mineral resources and energy. In Antarctica, over 200 deposits and pits are found, mainly iron, copper, nickel, chromium, lead, zinc, gold, silver and diamond. Among them, iron and copper have great prospects, and gold, silver and platinum metals have greater potential for prospecting. In Mount Charles Princess in East Antarctica, three large-scale and super large-scale iron deposits were found in an area of 200km^2, with average grades of 30–38%. They are Precambrian metamorphic iron deposits. In Antarctic Peninsula and South Shetland a lot of late mesozoic to Cenozoic copper, nickel, molybdenum, lead, zinc and gold deposits have been found. In Antarctic continental shelf regions, there are a lot of coal, petroleum, natural gas and natural gas hydrate[99].

In order to coordinate the investigation on mineral resources in Antarctica, the consultative countries of Antarctic Treaty held as of 1982 "*Special Consultative Meeting on Mineral Resources in Antarctica*". By May 1988, 12 sessions have been held (When China gained the status of signatory, it took part in the 8th and 9th Meeting). Finally, the "Convention on the Regulation of Antarctic Mineral Resources Activities" was made. The Treaty stipulates on the investigation, exploration and exploitation of mineral resources in the Antarctica. 33 countries signed the Convention. Due to the opposition of non-consultative countries of the Antarctic Treaty and environmentalists, the Convention didn't come into effect.

In order to protect the environment in the Antarctica, the "*Protocol on Environmental Protection to the Antarctic Treaty*" was passed in 1991.The Protocol has a special provision on the mineral resources activities in Antarctica. In Article Seven, "Any activities related to mineral resources activities are prohibited, excluding those for the purposes of scientific researches".

When the Protocol came into effect, the signatories have ceased their public mining activities, but the basic researches such as survey and exploration are still ongoing. With the depletion of resources in the continents in recent years, more and more attention is again given to the mineral resources in the Antarctica.

The term of the Protocol is 50 years. No one is sure about the orientation of development as to mineral resources in the Antarctica when the Protocol expires in early 2040s, but some countries are getting started for the preparation.

In early times, China had some expeditions for the purposes of investigation of mineral resources in the Antarctica. The activities basically stopped in 1990s, and the geologic work reduced to a small amount. New international situations in expeditions in North and South Poles required us to conduct mineral resources investigations as soon as possible to safeguard our national interests.

The Arctic is in somewhat special situation. Many regions are clearly the territories claimed by other countries. In the agreements signed by China and Norway in 1920s, China acknowledged the Norway's sovereignty over Svalbard Peninsula, but is entitled to scientific research, investigation on mineral resources and exploitations in the region. The Arctic Yellow River Station was established under this Treaty. Svalbard Peninsula is abundant in coal and the offshore region abundant in petroleum. Lately, gold deposits have been found.

2) Mineral resources on the ocean floor

The polymetal nodules, such as cobalt, hydrothermal sulfide, on the ocean floor and natural gas hydrate resources are catching more and more attentions. All countries have set eyes on how to get them. It is believed that the metal resources that have the brightest prospects are cobalt-rich nodule and hydrothermal sulfide.

Since 1980s, there have been world-renowned organizations dedicated for investigations on oceanic mineral resources. They include Deep Ocean Resources Development Limited of Japan (DORD), Institute of Oceanology of France (IFREMER/AFERNOD), Marine Geology Production Association in South USSR (YUZHMORGEOLOGIA), Department of Ocean Development of India (DOD), International Ocean Metal Organization (Poland, Cuba, Bulgaria, Czech, Slovakia and USSR), Ministry of Trade and Energy of South Korea (KORDI), etc. Some consortia in such countries as the USA, Britain, Germany, Italy, Netherlands and Belgium have conducted some investigations on such submarine resources as polymetal nodule and exploitation technologies, and thus having great investment potential. Germany led to the world in expedition and investigation on cobalt-rich nodules in the Pacific as early as in 1981, followed by the USA, Russia and France. In late 1980s and early 1990s, South Korea collaborated with the USA in investigation and study on cobalt-rich nodules in the West Pacific. At present, many countries are carrying out their investigations on cobalt-rich nodules.

Studies show that cobalt-rich nodules are another kind of important marine resources after polymetal nodule deposits in the ocean. They are mainly distributed in sea mount and submarine ridge regions of the three major oceans in the world. The nodules in the sea mount areas on both sides of the equator in the Pacific are the richest. The volume of the resources in the world is still immeasurable. However, in the volcanic uplift belt in the west of the Central Pacific, it is estimated that there are 1 billion tons of cobalt-rich nodules, which contain cobalt metal of millions of tons[100].

With the gradual depletion of terrestrial resources and development of science and technology, amidst the fierce competitions in the world, the areas where cobalt-rich nodules are distributed will surely be one of the important competition places by more and more economic, scientific and even political and military rivalries in the 21st century.

The China Ocean Mineral Resources Research and Development Association (COMRA) was founded in 1990, and has conducted investigations on submarine deposits. Since 1997, it has conducted over 10 voyage investigations, grasping the distribution characteristics and grade variations of cobalt-rich nodules in West and Central Pacific Ocean seamounts. Currently, it is conducting small-scale nodule grade variation studies in order to understand the distribution characteristics of the cobalt-rich nodules. The preparation for application of mining areas is under way. Currently, the level of China's research on cobalt-rich nodule resources is still very low; especially the investigation area and degree are inferior to other leading investors. The basic researches on metallogenesis of the cobalt-rich nodules are weak and the understanding of metallogenic mechanism is still unclear. Our future goal is to intensify and speed up the efforts in investigation of cobalt-rich nodules to get enough information and to get China prepared for applying a permit of exploitation from ISA.

From 1996 to 2007, the USA, Japan, Britain, Germany, France and Russia have in succession discovered a number of new submarine hydrothermal sulfide areas in the Pacific Ocean, Indian Ocean, Iceland and New Zealand. This has expanded the spatial distribution of submarine hydrothermal sulfides and extended our understanding of the distribution regularity.

With the help of advanced instruments and equipments and pertinent deep sea drilling plan, it is necessary to strengthen the systematic investigation and study on slow and super-slow spreading ocean ridges, off-axis oceanic crust, back-arc basin spreading centers, arc terrain, hotspot and transform fault zone. To conduct large-scale mapping and to understand the submarine hydrothermal activities and global metallogenic characteristics will be the basis for investigating and discovering new submarine hydrothermal sulfide distribution area.

In recent years, international investigations and study on the modern submarine hydrothermal sulfide mainly focus on to find new submarine hydrothermal sulfide distribution area, to research various aspects of the submarine hydrothermal sulfides, to carry out long-term monitoring of submarine hydrothermal activities and the sulfide formation, and to develop the advanced and new technologies for the investigations and researches on submarine hydrothermal sulfides.

The submarine hydrothermal sulfide is mainly distributed in mid-oceanic ridges and back-arc basins. The discovered modern submarine hydrothermal sulfide deposits are mainly distributed in the mid-oceanic ridge of the Pacific, Atlantic ridge, Pacific back-arc basin at about 1,000–4,000m deep below the sea level. Metal elements such as Cu, Zn, Pb, Au, Ag, Co, Ni and Pt are coexisted in the sulfide deposits which have been paid high attention by many countries. Mining companies in Australia and Canada have begun to invest or to get ready to start investment.

China has conducted preliminary investigations and researches on the hydrothermal activities and its sulfide resources in Okinawa Trough, Mariana Trough, East Pacific Rise, Atlantic Ridge and Southwest and Central Indian Ocean Ridge. China has completed plotting of maps of submarine hydrothermal sulfide "deposits" evaluation, proposed the target areas of prospecting in international sea-bed areas, conducted researches on mineralogy, petrology and geochemistry, and had geochemical comparison with the mineral deposits on the continents. Under the support of the National High Technology Research and Development Program ("863"Program) of China, researches and developments on manned submarines, TV grab bucket, ROV and other new and high technologies, that can be applied to the research and investigation of submarine hydrothermal sulfide, have been conducted during the "Tenth Five Year Plan". A platform for undertaking several kinds of simulation experiments including the water-rock interaction, hydrothermal plume diffusion and others upon interfacing with on-site hydrothermal fidelity sampler has been developed independently. This provides technical support for the researches on various aspects including the hydrothermal sulfide metallogenic mechanism and results in a substantive progress on investigation of submarine hydrothermal sulfide.

However, we should clearly realize that we have a 30-year long gap from developed countries in terms of submarine deposits investigation and researches. Once there arise practices of application for registing sulfide mining areas in the world, China will be in a very disadvantageous situation. How to narrow the gap and to gain an advantageous position in the competition for submarine sulfide resources in the future has been a problem that China must confront and tackle as soon as possible.

2.6.3 Overall Objectives and Objectives at Different Stages to 2050

(1) Overall Objectives

The overall objectives are to provide scientific basis for global allocation strategy of the mineral resources in China through studies on the formation and distribution regularities of global mineral resources, in particular the distribution regularities of mineral resources in neighboring countries in the north, African continent, the oceans and polar regions, in the combination of the distribution of the storage, production, transportation and trading of the global resources and the building of the market information network of the demand and supply.

(2) Objectives at Different Stages

1) From present to 2020

① To establish storage, production, transportation and trading distribution network for global resources and demand, supply and market information network, including import and export security and warning countermeasures; ② To put priority to neighboring countries which is the basic tactics for better utilization of overseas resources, to make and to improve the mineral resources supply channel with neighboring countries in the north as soon as possible, and to establish transnational mineral resources security bases in the north; ③ To establish steady mineral resources strategic partnership with friendly countries, to conduct overseas geologic survey in forms of various types, sole and joint exploration and development mechanism with the priority partners in Africa and South America; ④ To conduct researches on polar regions as the routine program, and to study the types and distribution of deposits; ⑤ To intensify investigations and researches on submarine polymetal nodules, cobalt-rich nodules and hydrothermal sulfide deposits.

2) From 2020 to 2030

① Further to strengthen the scientific and technological cooperation in the global context, to respond to the challenges posed by the widening of mineral resources types, the innovation of technologies in exploitation and utilization and the substitution and utilization of new alternative resources in the new situations,, to strengthen the international standing of China under the global economic law and framework; ② To study the conditions for developing resources in polar regions, to determine the resources exploitation bases and to conduct protective exploitation; ③ To ascertain the quantity and distribution characteristics of major mineral resources in the ocean, and to improve the exploitation technologies and to put them into small-scale application.

3) From 2030 to 2050

① To build global mineral resources safe utilization platform; ② To explore and exploit the mineral resources in open seas and polar regions under permission; ③ To intensify cooperation on space science and technology in order to make preparation for the exploration and utilization of possible extraterrestrial resources.

2.6.4 Major Scientific and Technological Issues to be Solved to Attain the Objectives

(1) Palaeozoic Asian Metallogenic Provinces and Global Tectonics and Metallogenic Dynamics

1) Geodynamic evolution and metallogenesis of the Palaeozoic Asian metallogenic provinces

In order to promote the regional economic integration and mineral resources distribution integration among members of the SCO, it is necessary to take the Palaeozoic Asian tectonic and metallogenic province as a whole body to study the opening, evolution, closure, orogeny and the full process of the post-orogeny transformation of the Palaeozoic Asian Ocean, to elucidate the metallogeny and mineral distribution regularity of this process, and to provide theoretical basis for the mineral resources required for the common development of the regional economy.

2) Geodynamic evolution and minerals distribution in African continent

The African continent is composed by ancient African platform and part of Alpine fold belts. The Africa in Mesozoic and Cenozoic is mainly affected by Gondwana cracking and the formation of continental margin and marginal basin along the Atlantic, Indian Ocean, Red Sea and Gulf of Aden. When the Cretaceous began, large-scale fracture occurred in the African continental interiors, forming in succession the West Central African Rift and the East African Rift, the two largest continental rifts in the world which are still in action.

In the African platform there are a lot of exposed fundamental series, which are mostly lack of covered beds. The Precambrian base is rich in mineral resources. New minerals were added into the Precambrian base since Cretaceous through magmatism, sedimentation and weathering. These make the Africa known as the "world natural resources warehouse". However, the resources in Africa have not yet been efficiently exploited and utilized. Africa has all of the 50 major minerals in the world with the reserves of at least 17 kinds of minerals ranked No.1 in the world.

The Precambrian metallogenesis and Cretaceous rifting-magmatic metaollogenesis of the African continent is a subject that is in urgent need of study.

3) Researches on global metallogeny

The metallogenesis possesses at once regional features and temporal features. Therefore, it is very necessary to carry out detailed researches on comparative metallogeny through international correlation programs in order to establish systematic metallogenic theories and to better understand the spatial and temporal distribution regularities of mineral resources.

(2) Researches on the Metallogenic Theories and Regularities in the Seabed, Polar Regions, and Shared Areas of Human Beings

It is necessary to study the metallogenic environment and mechanism for major mineral resources in the seabed, to reveal the distribution regularities of major mineral resources in the ocean, to develop the submarine observation, detection and drilling technologies for investigating submarine resources, to establish 3D observation network and supporting land-based and sea-based experimental observation platform in order to improve the predictive ability to the multi-metallogenic provinces in the ocean, to work out the long-term plan for basic researches on investigating and prospecting mineral resources in the Polar Regions, to incorporate the survey of mineral resources into our polar expedition plans, to reveal the distribution regularities of major mineral resources in the Polar Regions, to conduct survey on the distribution characteristics of mineral resources on the moon and Mars, to outline the anomalous zones of mineral resources on the moon and Mars, and to conduct pilot researches on developing and utilization of the resources.

(3) Related Software Science Researches

1) To analyze global distribution and allocation of mineral resources, and to analyze the per capita distribution, economic development and politics of countries, groups and regions that store, produce and trade these minerals.

2) To analyze the distribution of short-term, medium-term and long-term strategic minerals urgently needed by China, to analyze the supply, demand and prices of the international markets, and the affordable capacity and cost.

3) To evaluate degrees of prospecting, reserves of resources, supply capacity, resources potential and environmental effect of the Third World and friendly countries.

4) To predict degrees of prospecting, reserves of resources and supply capacity of the neighboring countries, and to evaluate their resources potential

and environmental effect.

5) To analyze the feasibility of joint venture or independent investment to establish basic mineral resources survey, exploration and exploitation bases in overseas.

6) To analyze the demands for dominant minerals of China in the world and their security countermeasures.

7) To analyze the international mineral resources market, supply capacity of minerals in China, dependence degree on overseas markets, warning mechanism and countermeasures in times of peace, stress and emergency, and block minerals strategic reserves.

8) To analyze the contributions to the mineral resources, trend of changes of demands and contradiction between supply and demand affected by the global science development in the future.

9) To analyze the safety issues of the supply channels for overseas mineral resources.

2.6.5 Suggestions of Measures for the Promotion of Global Allocation of Resources

1) In the global context, it is necessary to make basic evaluations on the distribution and the supply capacity of geologic and mineral resources featuring "making the best use of two kinds of resources".

2) To make comprehensive analysis of the output, trade volume, secondary and multiple recovery volume, product price and trend, purpose, prospects and field, and of the trend of changes of demands in the world in various time scales of 20 years, 50 years and 100 years based on the proved mineral reserves in the world including China's dominant exported minerals. Based on the basic relationship between the resources reserves, output, consumption, trade and the national economic structure, trend of development, geopolitics, group interests, industrial structure, and wealth accumulation regularity of the industrialized countries and the emerging developing countries, to make systematic and scientific analysis of the situation of the supply and demand of mineral resources, basic trend, and contradictions at different time scales.

3) According to the *"Decision of the State Council on Strengthening Geological Work"* (2006), it is necessary to encourage capable domestic enterprises to conduct explorations and exploitations of major mineral resources abroad, to establish mining groups or companies with international competitiveness, to adopt multiple cooperation and exploration modes, and to strengthen China's capability for exploration and exploitation of mineral resources both at home and abroad.

4) To evaluate China's two markets configuration and development through geographical advantages, cooperation, competition and rivalry with surrounding countries, friendly countries and stake-holding countries or regions or groups, and to, propose global allocation and security strategy of mineral resources for China conforming to its national, people, and mineral

realities on the basis of scientific researches.

5) To carry out active resources diplomacy through establishing and developing cooperative relationship with countries abundant in resources, to develop and form the overseas investment and business environment favorable for Chinese resources-based enterprises, thus to establish strategic alliance with cooperation on resources as the bond. This is the natural extension of China's national interests. In essence, it is a chance that a rising China gives full play to its market forces and reallocates global resources to strive for common benefits of mankind.

3 Policies Required to Attain Objectives

3.1 To Expedite the Building of Industrial Technological Innovation System

It is necessary to establish technological innovation system that combines production, processing and research, in order to greatly improve China's independent innovation ability. Enterprises should increase the funding for research and development, set up R&D organizations, centers, alliances or institutes, unite universities to establish laboratories, industrial engineering research centers and various collaboration organizations on technological innovation. This is to activate fully the research institutes' advantages in technological innovation of mineral resources, and to enhance the innovation ability. Research institutes and universities should promote their cooperation and integration of resources to meet the enterprises' demands for technological innovation, and play their leading role in tackling scientific and technological problems.

3.2 To Strengthen Innovative Personnel Training and Team Building in the Field of Mineral Resources

It is necessary to strengthen the building of a team of scientists and technicians in order to provide intellectual and talent guarantee for independent innovation and improvement of innovation capability, to intensify the talented personnel training, to expedite the grooming of leading scientists, technicians and professionals with strategic visions, to attract high level talents from overseas, especially those technical experts for development research, based on the key scientific and technological projects, scientific bases and international cooperation projects, to intensify the integration of scientific innovation and talented personnel training, to encourage the cooperation between research institutes and universities for training research-oriented talents, whose capability of research and development and pioneering spirit will be cultivated in the practice of technological innovations. Mining groups and companies shall work out incentive policies to promote undergraduates, graduates with master and doctoral degrees to innovate in enterprises, to attract talents from research institutes and universities through research and development projects to conduct technological innovations in enterprises. Universities, especially key universities, should provide educational guarantee for disciplines of mining industry, and should pay long-term attention on various aspects including provision of faculty and curriculum and monitoring of teaching quality in order to form and maintain a standby personnel tank with sufficient, high quality and sustainable talents. They should train a certain number of experts who are familiar with geology and mineral resources in the neighboring countries, and strengthen the training of engineers special at both geology and mineral resources in order to enrich the geologic exploration teams. It is necessary to strengthen the training of state and local exploration staff and to improve the exploration efficiency.

3.3 To Increase the Funding for Technological Innovation

Funding of research and development is the fundamental guarantee for sustainable technological innovation. It is necessary to ensure the steady growth of funds for scientific and technological research and innovation on the condition of the remarkable increase of the integrated national strength in China. Following the increase of governmental funding for science and technology, enterprises should gradually increase funding for research and development, with a growth rate of funding for research and development in enterprises exceeding the growth rate of the sales income. The invested funds and resources should be mainly used to strengthen the building of innovation system, talent teams, scientific and technological platform and research and development on technology for efficient utilization of mineral resources.

3.4 To Strengthen the Building of Basic Scientific and Technological Platforms

Basic scientific and technological platforms include base for research laboratories, large-scale research facilities and instrumentation, scientific data and information system. They are the material basis for technological innovation. Through effective allocation and sharing, they will support the technological innovation for the industry. China should, based on the key scientific and research institutes and universities, increase the funding and strengthen the building of state key laboratories, research centers and research and development bases. It is necessary to conduct works for introduction, adsorption and digestion of the key equipment for the research exploration, exploitation and utilization of mineral resources, and self independent research and development works, to improve the level of automation, informatization and digitization of equipment through hard work.

3.5 To Standardize Management of Mining Industry and to Strengthen the Lawful Mining Administration

Firstly, it is necessary to rationalize the relations and to standardize the mining management. Special support should be given to develop a number of large-scale mining corporations. Key attention should be paid to strategic minerals, dominant minerals and important mining areas. It is necessary to expedite the industrial structure adjustment and to improve the concentration of production, to encourage large-scale enterprises to engage win-win combination in order to merge, acquire, reconstruct and reform the small and medium-sized enterprises, to encourage the development of large-scale transnational, trans-regional, trans-industrial, and trans-ownership mining corporations in order to activate the large-scale efficiency and benefit. Secondly, it is necessary to conduct work related to legislation, justice and law enforcement in terms of mineral resources, to adhere to lawful administration, to strengthen the intensity of lawful enforcement, and to provide lawful guarantee for rational utilization, effective protection and scientific management of mineral resources.

3.6 To Pay Attention to Overall Planning of Global Mineral Resources

Firstly, it is necessary to strengthen the establishment and research of the international correlation program on the metallogenesis, to promote the development of regional and global metallogeny. Secondly, it is necessary to introduce actively the advanced technology and mature experience for the exploration and exploitation, comprehensive utilization and mines management of the international resources. Thirdly, it's necessary to implement the "Go out" strategy for the mineral resources, to intensify researches, exploration and exploitation of overseas resources, to promote the international cooperation through various forms such as new projects, merging and acquisition, and equity participation, to reform the management mechanism of the "go out" strategic investment, and to facilitate the prospecting, development and investment of mineral resources.

3.7 To Set up Incentive Policies and Laws on the Development of New Resources Industry

The development of new resources industry depends on science, technology and policies. Technological innovation is the basis, and the policy support is the key factor for the development of new resources industry. It is suggested that China should start gradually the resources substitution and cyclic utilization blueprint, as it did in new energy industry, to start new resources industry configuration, to provide relevant supporting incentive policies and laws, including tax reliefs, preferential loan, project assistance, etc. by taking advantage of the occasion that "Recycling Economy Promotion Law of PRC" came into effect in january 2009.

3.8 To Set up Incentive Policies and Laws on Application of Technological Innovation

The modern information and communication technologies (ICT) have been rapidly developed and the applications of their achievements are quickly popularized in overall society. The earlier of the ICT achievements are applied into the mineral resources industry, the faster of the utilization of mineral resources could be practiced. For example, it is necessary to encourage to research and develop small, handy, portable, distribution-type and networking automatic data acquisition system and data processing system for mineral resources exploration, and various modern digitized detecting and acquiring systems of geology, geophysics, geochemistry and remote sensing, in order to acquire precise three-dimensional space information related to mineral resources. The formulation of state policies should reflect the incentive measures for application of the modern ICT achievements into the mineral resources and new resources industries.

4 Conclusion

China has both long-term huge demands on mineral resources and great mineral resources potential. However, at present, the level of research and exploration of mineral resources in China is still very low, and the level of the mineral resources utilization is quite low. Accordingly, some key scientific and technological programs in mineral resources field should be implemented in order to vigorously promote the innovation of metallogenic theories, exploration technologies, processing and smelting technologies, resources substitution and cyclic utilization technologies.

The basic idea of this roadmap is to highly emphasize the exploration and development of domestic mineral resources, meanwhile, to pay attention to utilize overseas mineral resources, to conduct research and exploration on mineral resources distributed in seabed and the polar regions at the right time, to strengthen researches on continental metallogeny and associated predictive prospecting, as well as on the clean and efficient utilization of traditional ores, low-grade ores, idle ores and associated ores, to initiate as soon as possible projects of the "Forecast and Exploration Program of the Mineral Resources in Depth" and "Resources Substitution and Cyclic Utilization Program", in order to climb the scientific peak of the mineral resources, to meet the strategic demand of China on mineral resources and to promote harmonious development between exploitation and utilization of mineral resources and ecological environment.

References

[1] Zeng PY. The State Council reports about rational utilization. protection and management of the mineral resources. The National People's Congress Standing Committee of the Communiqué, 2007, (1): 104–110 (in Chinese).

[2] Lei YL. The safety situation and its strategy of mineral resources in China. http://www.lrn.cn/stratage/resposition/200807/t20080717_254620.htm. [2008-07-17] (in Chinese).

[3] Chen YC. The situation and its strategy of mineral resources in China. Report of the third National Symposium on metallogenic theory and prospecting method, Haikou, 2007 (in Chinese).

[4] Yu XM. The Ministry of Land and Resources making guarantee strategies of bulk mineral resources. http: //www.cs.com.cn/ssgs/04/200810/t20081023_1630674.htm. [2008-10-23] (in Chinese).

[5] Wang LB ,Liu J .The degree of external dependence of important mine types in China presenting the downward trend. http://www.bid.sei.gov.cn/ShowArticle2008.asp?ArticleID=166423.[2008-10-22] (in Chinese).

[6] Yuan AG. Wang QF, Xu H. Analysis of actuality and approaches to the supplying capacity of domestic metal mineral resources. Resources & Industries, 2007, 9(2): 68–71 (in Chinese).

[7] Cui RG. Analysis of trade situation of mineral products in 2007. http://www.lrn.cn/bookscollection/magazines/maginfo/2008maginfo/qingbao200804/200809/t20080902_271297.htm. [2008-09-02] (in Chinese).

[8] Zhang Y. The value of Chinese foreign trade import and export more than 2 trillion dollars in 2007. http://finance.sina.com.cn/china/hgjj/20080111/15044395583.shtml. [2008-01-11] (in Chinese).

[9] Liu YQ, Qiao FS. Mineral resources, demand and supply of mining products in China and some suggestions. Mineral Resources and Geology, 2007, 21: 1–7 (in Chinese with English abstract).

[10] Xu SS. Overall planning, strengthening investigation and control, constantly improve the support ability of the economic society from mineral resources. National Land & Resources Information, 2007, (12): 19–21 (in Chinese).

[11] Zhai YS. Temporal-spatial evolution of metallogenic systems and its resource effect. Report of the third National Symposium on metallogenic theory and prospecting method, Haikou, 2007 (in Chinese).

[12] Xiao QH. Scientific objectives and frontier of the continental dynamics. Management on Geological Science and Technology, 1996, (3): 34–37 (in Chinese).

[13] Li JT, Xiao XC. Plate tectonic theory and continental dynamics. Geological Review, 1998, 44(4): 337–338 (in Chinese).

[14] Ding GY. New trends of continental dynamics in geoscience. The speech at the closing ceremony of '99 international symposium on Tianshan earthquakes, Inland Earthquake, 1999, 13(4): 289–290 (in Chinese).

[15] Liu BJ, Li TD. Some problem of geology. Advance in Earth Science, 2001, 6(5): 607–616 (in Chinese with English abstract).

[16] Zhang GW, Dong YP, and Yao AP. Some thoughts on the study of continental dynamics and orogenic belts. Geology in China, 2002, 29(1): 7–13 (in Chinese with English abstract).

[17] Teng JW. Deep structure of the earth, deep dynamic process and leading direction in China. Geological Review, 2002, 48(3): 125–139 (in Chinese with English abstract).

[18] Mitchell AHG, Garson MS. Mineral deposits and tectonic settings. London: Academic Press, 1981.

[19] Sawkins FG. Metal deposits in relation to plate tectonic.New York: Springer Verlag, 1984.

[20] Rudinck RL. Continental crust: growth from below. Nature, 1990, 347: 711–712.

[21] Oyarzun R, Márquez A, Lillo J, et al. Giant versus small porphyry copper deposits of Cenozoic age in northern Chile: adakitic versus normal calc-alkaline magmatism. Mineralium Deposita, 2001, 36:

794–798.

[22] Sazonov VN, van Herk AH, and Hugo de Boorder. Spatial and temporal distribution of gold deposits in the Urals. Economic Geology, 2001, 96: 685–703.

[23] Miao LC, Qiu YM, McNaughton N, et al. SHRIMP U-Pb zircon geochronology of granitoids from Dongping area, Hebei Province, China: constraints on tectonic evolution and geodynamic setting for gold metallogeny.Ore Geology Reviews, 2002, 19: 187–204.

[24] Ernst RE, Buchan KL. Recognizing mantle plume in the geological record. Ann. Rev. Earth and Planetary Science Letters, 2003, 31: 469–523.

[25] Sillitoe RH, Hedenquist JW. Linkages between volcanotectonic settings, ore-fluid compositions, and epithermal precious-metal deposits. In:Simmons S F (eds). Understanding crustal fluids: Roles and witnesses of processes deep within the earth, Giggenbach memorial volume: Society of Economic Geologists and Geochemical Society, Special Publication, 2003.

[26] Naldrett AJ. Magmatic sulfide deposits: geology, geochemistry and exploration. New York: Springer Verlag, 2004, 725.

[27] Song XY, Zhou MF, Keays RR, et al. Geochemistry of the Emeishan flood basalts at Yangliuping, Sichuan, SW China: implications for sulfide segregation. Contributions to Mineralogy and Petrology, 2006, 152 (1): 53–74.

[28] Song XY, Zhou MF, Tao Y, Xiao JF.Controls on the metal compositions of magmatic sulfide deposits in the Emeishan large igneous province, SW China.Chemical Geology, 2008, 253: 38–49

[29] Cooke DR, Hollings P, and Walsh JL. Giant porphyry deposits: characteristics, distribution, and tectonic controls. Economic Geology, 2005, 100 (5): 801–818.

[30] Blundell D, Arndt N, Cobbold PR, et al. Processes of tectonism, magmatism and mineralization: lessons from Europe. Ore Geology Reviews, 2005, 27 (1–4): 333–349

[31] Singer DA, Berger VI, Menzie WD, et al. Porphyry copper deposit density. Economic Geology, 2005, 100 (3): 491–514.

[32] Zieg MJ, Marsh BD. The sudbury igneous complex: viscous emulsion differentiation of a superheated impact melt sheet.Geological Society of America Bulletin, 2005, 117 (11–12): 1427–1450.

[33] Elsila JE, de Leon NP, Plows FL, et al. Extracts of impact breccia samples from Sudbury, Gardnos, and Ries impact craters and the effects of aggregation on C-60 detection.Geochimica et Cosmochimica Acta, 2005, 69 (11): 2891–2899.

[34] Sun WD, Ding X, Hu YH, and Li XH. The golden transformation of the Cretaceous plate subduction in the west Pacific. Earth and Planetary Science Letters, 2007, 262(3–4): 533–542.

[35] Chen YJ, Pirajno T, and Sui YH. Isotope geochemistry of the Tieluping silver-lead deposit, Henan, China: a case study of orogenic silver-dominated deposits and related tectonic setting. Mineralium Deposita, 2004, 39(5-6): 560–575.

[36] Hou ZQ, Zeng PS, Gao YF, et al. Himalayan Cu-Mo-Au mineralization in the eastern Indo-Asian collision zone: constraints from Re-Os dating of molybdenite. Mineralium Deposita, 2006, 41 (1): 33–45.

[37] Hou ZQ, Tian SH, Yuan ZX, et al. The Himalayan collision zone carbonatites in western Sichuan, SW China: Petrogenesis, mantle source and tectonic implication.Earth and Planetary Science Letters, 2006, 244 (1–2): 234–250.

[38] Zhang GW, Zhang BR, Yuan XC, et al. Qinling orogenic zone and continental dynamics.Beijing: Science Press, 2001 (in chinese).

[39] Wang JB, Xu X. Post-collisional tectonic evolution and metallogenesis in Northern Xinjiang, China. ACTA Geologica Sinica, 2006, 80(1): 23–31

[40] Naldrett AJ, Lightfoot PC. Ni-Cu-PGE deposits of the Noril'sk region, Siberia; their formation in conduits for flood basalt volcanism. In: Keays RR, Lesher CM, Lightfoot PC, and Farrow CEG(eds.). Dynamic processes in magmatic ore deposits and their application in mineral

exploration, Ottawa, Geological Association of Canada, Short Course Volume 13, 1999, 195–249.
[41] Hua RM,Mao JW. A preliminary discussion on the Mesozoic metallogenic explosion in East China. Mineral Deposits, 1999, 18(4): 300–308 (in Chinese with English abstract).
[42] Mao JW, Wang ZL. A preliminary study on time limits and geodynamic setting of large-scale metallogeny in East China. Mineral Deposits, 2000, 19(4): 289–296 (in Chinese with English abstract).
[43] Mao JW, Zhang ZH, Yu JJ, et al.The geodynamic setting of the Mesozoic large scale mineralization in North China: revelation from precision dating of the metal deposits.Science in China (series D), 2003, 33(4): 289–300 (in Chinese).
[44] Mao JW, Xie GQ, Li XF, et al. Geodynamic process and metallogeny: history and present research trend with a special discussion on continental accretion and related metallogeny throughout geological history in South China. Mineral Deposits, 2005, 24(3): 193–205 (in Chinese with English abstract).
[45] Hu RZ, Bi XW, Peng JT, et al. Some problems concerning relationship between Mesozoic-Cenozoic lithospheric extension and uranium metallogenesis in South China. Mineral Deposits, 2007, 26(2): 139–152 (in Chinese with English abstract).
[46] Hu RZ, Bi XW, Zhou MF, et al. Uranium metallogenesis in South China and its relationship to crustal extension during the Cretaceous to Tertiary.Economic Geology, 2008,103: 583–598.
[47] Groves DI, Goldfarb RJ, Gebre-Mariam M, et al. Orogenic gold deposits: a proposed classification in the context of their crustal distribution and relationship to other gold deposit types. Ore Geology Reviews, 1998, 13 (1–5): 7–27.
[48] Degens ET, Ross DA. Hot brines and recent heavy metal deposits of the Red Sea. New York: Springer-Verlag, 1969.
[49] Shanks WC, Bischoff JL. Ore transport and deposition in the Red Sea geothermal system: a geochemical model. Geochimica et Cosmochimica Acta, 1977, 41: 1507–1519.
[50] James DE, Sack IS. Cenozoic formation of the central Andes: a geophyscial perspective. In: Skinner B J (eds). Geology and ore deposits of the central Andes. Soc. Econ. Geol. Spec. Pub. 1999, 7: 1–25.
[51] Kerrich R, Goldfarb R, Groves D, et al. The characteristics,origins and geodynamic settings of supergiant gold metallogenic provinces. Science in China (series D), 2000, 43(supp.):1–68.
[52] Goldfarb RJ, Groves DI, and Cardoll S. Orogenic gold and geologic time: a global synthesis. Ore Geol. Rev., 2001, 18:1–75.
[53] Ulrich T, Gunther D, and Heinrich CA.The evolution of a porphyry Cu-Au deposit, based on LA-ICP-MS analysis of fluid inclusions: Bajo de la albumbrera, Argentina. Economic Geology, 2001, 96: 1743–1774.
[54] Heinrich CA, Driesner T, Stefansson A, et al. Magmatic vapor contraction and the transport of gold from the porphyry environment to epithermal ore deposits. Geology, 2004, 32(9): 761–764.
[55] Stein HJ, Morgan JW, and Schersten A. Re-Os dating of low-level highly radiogenic (LLHR) sulfides; the Harnas gold deposit, Southwest Sweden, records continental-scale tectonic events. Economic Geology, 2000,95(8): 1657–1671.
[56] Zhu XK, O'Nions RK, Guo Y, et al. Determination of natural Cu-isotope variation by plasma-source mass spectrometry: implications for use as geochemical tracers.Chemical Geology, 2000, 163: 139–149.
[57] Johnson CM, Beard BL, and Albarede F. Geochemistry of non-traditional stable isotopes. Mineralogical Society of America, Washington, 2004, 1–434.
[58] Kesler SE, Riciputi LC, and Ye ZJ. Evidence for a magmatic origin for Carlin-type gold deposits: isotopic composition of sulfur in the Betze-Post-Screamer deposit, Nevada, USA. Mineralium Deposita, 2005, 40: 127–136.
[59] Frank MR. Gold solubility, speciation, and partitioning as a function of HCl in the brine-silicate melt-metallic gold system at 800°C and 100MPa. Geochimica et Cosmochimica Acta, 2002, 66:

3719–3723.
[60] Hack AC, Mavrogenes JA. A synthetic fluid inclusion study of copper solubility in hydrothermal brines from 525 to 725°C and 0.3 to 1.7GPa. Geochimica et Cosmochimica Acta, 2006, 70: 3970–3985.
[61] Faure G. Principles and applications of geochemistry. New Jersey:Prentice-Hall, Inc., 1998.
[62] Henley RW, Berger BR. Self-ordering and complexity in epizonal mineral deposits. Annual Review of Earth and Planetary Sciences, 2000, 28: 669–719.
[63] Titley SR.The style and progress of mineralization and alteration in porphyry copper systems. In: Titley SR(eds). Advances in geology of the porphyry copper deposits: Tucson: University of Arizona Press, 1982, 93–116.
[64] Franklin JM, Lydon JW, and Sangster DF. Volcanic-associated massive sulfide deposits. Economic Geology, 1981, 75th Anniversary Volume: 485–627.
[65] Hausen DF, Kerr PF. Fine gold occurrence at Carlin, Nevada. In: Ridge JD (eds). Ore Deposits of the United States, 1933–1967, Vol.1, AIME, 1968, 908–940.
[66] Zhai YS, Yao SC, and Cui B. Research on metallogenic.Beijing: China University of Geosciences Press, 1996 (in Chinese).
[67] Zhai YS, et al. Regional metallogeny. Beijing:Geological Publishing House, 1999 (in Chinese).
[68] Tu GZ, et al. Super-large deposits in China (I).Beijing: Science Press, 1999 (in Chinese).
[69] Chen YC, et al. Preliminary discussion on minerogenetic series of mineral deposits in China. Beijing: Geological Publishing House, 1998 (in Chinese).
[70] Chen YC, Pei RF, Wang DH, et al. On minerogenetic (metallogenetic) series: third discussion. ACTA Geologic Sinica, 2006, 80(10): 1501–1508 (in Chinese with English abstract).
[71] Tu GZ, et al. Low temperature geochemistry.Beijing: Science Press, 1998 (in Chinese).
[72] Tu GZ, Li CY.Brief remarks on comparative metallogeny. Geochemical, 2000, 35(1): 1–5 (in Chinese with English abstract).
[73] Shi JF, Xiao QH. Development trends of empiricism exploration and concept exploration. Regional Geology of China, 2003, 23(8): 809–815 (in Chinese with English abstract).
[74] Zhang HR, Fan ZG. Recent adcances in aerogeophysical techniques used abroad. Geophysical and Geochemical Exploration, 2007, 31(1): 1–8 (in Chinese with English abstract).
[75] Cameron EM, Hamilton SMH, Leybourne MIL, et al. Finding deeply-buried deposits using geochemistry. Geochemistry-exploration, Environment, Analysis, 2004, 4(1) : 7–32.
[76] Xie XJ, Wang XQ. Recent development on deep penetrating geochemistry. Earth Science Frontiers, 2003, 10(1): 225–238 (in Chinese with English abstract).
[77] Zhou SP. Review and discussion on basic and applied geological research, exploration and development of metallic mineral resources in Australia. Advances in Earth Science, 2006, 21(4): 436–439 (in Chinese with English abstract).
[78] He ZX, et al. New progress and application of integrative geophysical survey techniques. Oil Geophysical Prospecting, 2005, 41(1): 108–112 (in Chinese with English abstract).
[79] Liu SC. Towards the next generation of giant minerals exploration techniques: some considerations about the glass earth. Geology and Prospecting, 2003, 39(5): 53–56 (in Chinese with English abstract).
[80] Chen J, Wen N, and Chen BY. Joint inversion of gravity-magnetic-electrical-seismic combination survey: progress and prospect. Progress in Geophysics, 2007,(5): 1427–1438 (in Chinese with English abstract).
[81] Cheng ZP. A course of electric prospecting. Beijing: Metallurgical Industry Press, 2007 (in Chinese).
[82] Feng X, Li G, and Qiu G. A preliminary study on mercury contamination to the environment from Artisanal Zinc smelting using indigenous method in Hezhang County, Guizhou, China. Part 1 mercury emission from zinc smelting and its influences on the surface water. Atmospheric

Environment, 2004, 38: 6223–6230.

[83] Bi X, Feng X, Yang Y, Qiu G, and Li Z. Quantitative assessment of cadmium emission from zinc smelting and its influences on the surface soils and mosses in Hezhang County, Southwestern China. Atmospheric Environment, 2006, 40: 4228–4233.

[84] Qiu G, Feng X, Wang S, and Shang L. Environmental contamination of mercury from Hg-mining areas in Wuchuan, Northeastern Guizhou, China. Environmental Pollution, 2006, 142: 549–558.

[85] Li P, Feng X, Qiu G, Shang L, Wang S, and Meng B. Atmospheric mercury emission from artisanal mercury mining in Guizhou Province, Southwestern China. Atmospheric Environment, 2009, doi:10.1016/j.atmosenv.2009.01.050.

[86] Feng X, Qiu G. Mercury pollution in Guizhou, China— an overview. Science of the Total Environment, 2008, 400: 227–237.

[87] Feng X, Li P, Qiu G, Wang S, Li G, Shang L, Meng B, Jiang H, Bai W, Li Z, and Fu X. Methylmercury exposure through rice intake to inhabitants in Wanshan mercury mining area in Guizhou, China. Environmental Science and Technology, 2008, 42: 326–332.

[88] Qiu G, Feng X, Li P, Wang S, Li G, Shang L, and Fu X. Methylmercury accumulation in rice (*Oryza sativa* L.) grown at abandoned mercury mines in Guizhou, China.Journal of Agriculture and Food Chemistry, 2008, 56: 2465–2468.

[89] Liu JM, et al. Examples of unconventional mineral resources in China and the related scientific key-points. Progress in Geophysics, 2001, 16(4): 133–143 (in Chinese with English abstract).

[90] Yi XS, et al. Composite materials engineering. Beijing: Chemical Industry Press, 2006, 1044 (in Chinese).

[91] Yi YS, Chen SG, and Li J. Advanced structural materials and composites. Beijing: Chemical Industry Press, 2006, 296 (in Chinese).

[92] Fu ZY, Li JB. Advanced ceramics and inorganic non-metallic materials. Beijing: Science Press, 2007, 555 (in Chinese).

[93] Yang CY. Light metal metallurgy. Beijing: Metallurgical Industry Press, 2007, 336 (in Chinese).

[94] Jin DY. Practice and exploration of the regeneration resources industry. Beijing: China Environmental Science Press, 2001(in Chinese).

[95] Zhang H, Hu DW. Conditions and development potentialities of China's secondary resource recycling. Metal Mine, 2004, supplementary issue: 29–33 (in Chinese with English abstract).

[96] The editorial board of "Comprehensive utilization manual of mineral resources". Comprehensive utilization manual of mineral resources. Beijing: Science Press, 2002, 835(in Chinese).

[97] Wang JA, Wang GS, et al. Mineral resources and national economic development. Beijing: Earthquake Press, 2002(in Chinese).

[98] Development Research Center of China Geological Survey. Deal with the globalization: one of the information system database of global mineral resources. 2004, 296 (in Chinese).

[99] Li YS. Brief remarks on the problem of polar mineral resources, Report on the Symposium of the strategy of technology development in the field of national mineral resources in the future 50 years, 2008,Beijing (in Chinese).

[100] Zeng ZG.Situations report and some problems about the submarine mineral resources, Report on the Symposium of the strategy of technology development in the field of national mineral resources in the future 50 years, 2008,Beijing (in Chinese).

Epilogue

The Chinese Academy of Sciences (CAS) has organized strategic researches on roadmaps for the scientific and technological development of many important fields from present to 2050. This is of great significance and strategic vision. With more than one year's efforts, the Solid Mineral Resources Project Team has worked out a strategic research report entitled by "*Mineral Resources Science in China: A Roadmap to 2050*". It provides a comprehensive analysis of the solid mineral resources situation in China and a systematic description of the status-quo and development trend of the five major orientations in China's mineral resources field. Moreover, it generalizes the key scientific and technological issues on the five orientations, and clarifies the main technological means to resolve these issues. Based on these, it proposes the overall objectives and the objectives at various stages and the suggestions for main policies to attain the objectives. It is foreseeing, directional and operable. It is noteworthy that the compilation of a roadmap for the scientific and technological development is a strategic, forseeing and comprehensive systematic project. As members of the project team might not have mature experience and full knowledge of this area in some extent, there might be some mistakes and shortcomings in the report. It would be grateful if they are pointed out. The good news is that this project is still ongoing. It is believed that some improvements in the following areas in the future researches should be made.

1) To further demonstrate the demands on bulk strategic minerals by China in different stages and then to further discuss in detail what kind of routes should be selected for ensuring China's demands on mineral resources in the future.

2) To further make up detailed plans for researches on planetary mineral resources, including the metallogenesis, exploration and utilization potential of mineral resources of the moon and the Mars, to further work out plan for researches on the global allocation of resources in oceans and the polar regions, in order to improve upon the roadmap.

3) There are complicated and unique geologic conditions in China, especially the geologic evolution and metallogenesis of the special metallogenic system in China. This requires us to further sort out scientific issues with China's geologic characteristics, to understand metallogenic regularities, and to create metallogenic theories suitable to China's geologic characteristics in order to supervising exploration and prospecting of mineral resources in China,

on the basis of the roadmap and the consideration of the various metallogenic provinces and special metallogenic systems in China.

4) Based on the geologic, topographic and morphological characteristics of China, we need to further develop the crucial technologies compatible to China's prospecting reality and the optimal probing technologies for the different types of deposits in different depths. We should especially understand clearly where the crucial technologies are in the development of geophysical exploration methods, and further understand which problems of the crucial technologies should be overcome in different stages.

5) In terms of clean and efficient utilization of mineral resources, we need to further improve the key technological issues regarding mining, energy conservation, discharge reduction and environmental restoration of the mines, and improve the main means for solving those problems.

6) On the basis of the roadmap, we should focus the research on basic, strategic, pilot and systematic key issues of science and technology in the area, especially clarify the strategic objectives from present to 2020 (i.e., the "12th and 13th Five Year Plans"), and then figure out a detailed roadmap for the development of the solid mineral resources from present to 2020.

Roadmap study is a dynamic process. We believe that the roadmap made and revised on the basis of undertaking more and more detailed researches will be more conformable to the actual track of the development of the solid mineral resource in the future.

FSC
www.fsc.org
MIX
Papier | Fördert gute Waldnutzung
FSC® C083411

Kolibri 360 GmbH
Ferdinand-Jühlke-Straße 7
99095 Erfurt, Deutschland
produktsicherheit@kolibri360.de